THE GUIDE TO EATING AND DRINKING IN DUBLIN

Also in this Series :

Edibilia : The Guide to Eating Out in Oxford

Forthcoming guides in this Series :

Edibilia : The Guide to Eating in Galway
Edibilia : The Guide to Eating in Cork

EDIBILIA

The Guide to Eating and Drinking in Dublin

"Any restaurant that is open to do business is open to be judged. I've never seen a restaurant mark down its prices because the chef felt he wasn't on top form that day"

- Loyd Grossman
on restaurants having "off days"

Compiled by Ian McClean
Series Editor Bernadette Doyle
Published by Edibilia Publishing

First published in 1993
by
Edibilia Publishing,
25 Palmerston Place,
Dublin 7.

Book Design by Tony Moreau

Cover Design by Cathy Dineen

Typeset by Juliette Moreau

Printed by Guernsey Press

ISBN 1 873273 01 0

Distributed in conjunction with Poolbeg Press

Contents

Daytime 1
Chips with Everything 19
Pizza 'n Pasta 24
American 30
French 34
Indian 38
Irish 42
Italian 44
Oriental 55
Exotic 67
Wholefood 74
Seafood 78
Culture Vultures 85
Glitterati 91
Pretenders 100
Old Reliables 108
Out of Town 115
Curiosities 128
Hotels 134
Pubs 142
Reader Contribution Form 161
Index 163

Acknowledgements

Sincere thanks are extended to everybody who made the publication of this book possible. A great appreciation is offered to all restaurant / pub owners and managers for providing factual information and, in certain cases, advertising support without which this exercise would not have been viable.

- Editorial thanks to Carolyn McGrath and posse, Laura George, Fran Power, Orna Mulcahy; Nigel Werner, John Colclough, Gwen McGowan and Ciara Kierans.
- Section Introductions' thanks to Marilyn Bright and Caroline Martin.
- Research, Review and Advertising thanks to Alister Brèdée, Noele McEvoy, Diane Jacobs and SylviaThompson.
- Administrative thanks to Niamh Hegarty and Ruth Chamberlain.
- Typesetting thanks to Tony Moreau and Andy Gilsenan for inspiration well beyond duty's call and to Juliette Moreau for ads and patience.
- Facilitative thanks to Image Magazine, Evening Herald, Hot Press, U Magazine, FM 104 and all the contributions inspired by their competitions.
- Illustrative thanks to Cathy Dineen for the fab cover, and to Shane Johnson.
- Special thanks to all who submitted editorial for consideration especially Ruth Chamberlain and Róisín Banville.
- Very special thanks to series editor Bernadette Doyle for mapping out the territory.
- Finally, to all those who believed it would never work, thank you for the reserves of persistence and inspiration necessary to prove it would.

INTRODUCTION

'dibilia's Objective

Listing information on every eating establishment in Dublin*, Edibilia is the .rst-ever comprehensive guide to food in the capital with a selection of some of ıe finer pubs.

Edibilia is not designed as a gourmet guide but instead is designed for anyone ating out on a regular or semi-regular basis who would like to experiment out- ide the 'old reliables', but is, not surprisingly, deterred by unknown factors like rice, service quality, food quality etc. Edibilia acts as both a directory to any basic ıformation on any restaurant (e.g. opening/closing times, seating capacity, aver- ge cost of meals etc.) and also tries to convey a sense of place in terms of atmos- here, decor, service, food and value together with anything else worthy of note.

Edibilia, therefore, is tailored as an objective, unbiased guide for the lay person) allow experimentation with a choice of new restaurants in some confidence nd security. On the thorny subject of advertising: as overseer of this entire pro- ect I can solemnly state that inclusion in Edibilia is entirely free of charge, that nybody who chose to advertise do so in support of the concept and that their ecision to advertise (or not) in no way impacted the editorial. There are many xamples in the guide which prove our objectivity.

Iaking a meal of it

In Ireland today eating out is seen more and more as a form of social entertain- ıent, with knowledge and awareness of food and wines improving rapidly. estaurant standards, thankfully, have improved as a consequence, as indeed has ıe number of new restaurants. Eating out , however, is not just about food, and ıere are many influencing factors which determine whether the occasion is a suc- ess or otherwise - cost, value, decor, service, ambience and, of course, the com- any you are with all have a bearing on your overall enjoyment.

)ne man's meat ...

In truth there is no such thing as total objectivity when reviewing restaurants, s simply by expressing an opinion you are being subjective. Our contributors ave at times offered us conflicting views of the same restaurants (sometimes on ıe same evening!). In light of this our comments are not heavily judgemental - xcept where glaringly necessary - but rather attempt to describe each establish- ıent as accurately as possible and give an account of what people can expect in reas like cost, value, decor, service, presentation and ambience.

:very effort has been made by Edibilia to contact every establishment in Dublin serving significant food. Edibilia accepts responsibility for any omissions that have occurred as a result of any establishment failing to co operate or heed desig- ted deadlines.

Ratings

We have not used a ratings system in this guide. This is because our coverag ranges from snack bars and fish and chip shops to internationally acclaime restaurants like Patrick Guilbaud's. It would be misleading and unfair to bot restaurant owners and readers to adopt a rating system which applied equal rule to both. Instead we have judged establishments on what they are trying to do an how well they do it.

HOW TO USE THIS GUIDE

The Right Restaurant

If you are looking for information on a particular restaurant, you will find i most easily by looking up the name in the index at the back of this book Sometimes you may be looking for a suggestion rather than a particular restau rant.

To help readers find the most appropriate establishments we have organised th guide into sections such as 'Pizzas' or 'Seafood' which are listed in the content page. If you are looking for a type of restaurant which doesn't have its own sec tion, such as Spanish, Greek or Lebanese, the index will direct you to the correc review page.

Categorisation

To categorise some 600 entries into easily definable sections was in some way the most onerous task involved. Our first object was to classify restaurants by type (of food served) - French, Italian, Oriental etc. Some of the categories we ha to forge ourselves, and we have tried to be both imaginative and informative i our creation e. g. Glitterati, Pretenders, Curiosities and Old Reliables. As a help each section is prefaced with a short introduction which we are sure will be o value.

Format

Information on each restaurant is divided in two - Basic information (italics and Review. Details of location, opening times, prices and payment appear befor the Review while a list of special services/facilities feature after.

Basic Information

For the most part self-explanatory except for pricing. A price will appear afte the word "Average" - this indicates the average cost of a three course mea (starter/ main course/dessert) without wine or coffee. It is designed to give a con sistent benchmark and indicator as to how much one can expect to pay for th verage-priced meal in advance of the visit. Be aware, however, that you could ine for more or less than this figure depending on your choices.

redit Cards

he following abbreviations apply:-

(Access) AmEx (American Express) V (Visa) DC (Diners Club)
C (Eurocheque) LV (Luncheon Voucher) TC (Travellers Cheque).

ON WINE

he object of this short wine section is to overcome much of the hang up and inhi-ition we, as Irish, suffer when it comes to ordering wine. Not destined to make ou an overnight sommelier, it will, however, offer a slightly greater awareness f grape varieties and their regions and also make some helpful suggestions on hat foods compliment what wines.....or whatever you're having yourself !!

Vine not?

he past ten years have seen the most exciting developments in the world of wine. he rise in popularity of "New World Wines" has brought with it a greatly increased wareness and appreciation of wine.

Many restaurants are now offering a great variety of wines at under £10 a bot-e. House wines such as Chilean, Italian, Spanish, French, Australian, Bulgarian nd South African are super value and well worth exploring.

The rise in popularity of New World wine has affected the traditional areas of urope, in particular France. The French are now fighting back from the region of anguedoc Rousillon in the South of France. This used to be the area for produc-ng vast quantities of the cheapest and lowest quality table wines. Recent years ave seen extensive replanting of vines with new wineries producing excellent uality wines under the Vin de Pays banner. These wines are well worth seeking ut and sell for between £9 and £12 in restaurants where they are often featured s wines of the month.

The £10 to £15 category is probably the most exciting part of Adventurous estaurateurs' lists, as this is where most diners make their selection. Here New Vorld wines predominate, like Australia's Oxford Landing wines or Lindemans; hile's Concha y Toro or Errazuriz to mention a few.

Despite the New World influence, the leading wine producing countries are till France and Italy. The classic regions of France are maintaining their strong-old although some areas are wrongly neglected, in particular Alsace, whose vines are deliciously fruity and aromatic (Pinot Blanc, Riesling and Gewürz-räminer from the famous houses of Schlumberger, Hugel and Trimbach). There s also a new wave of interest in Italian wines which are great value due to the veakness of the lire.

Restaurant lists are improving all the time, and many now give descriptions r notes on their wines which is very helpful to assist customers in their choice. here is also greater knowledge than ever, with better-trained wine waiters, who re better able to make recommendations and impart their experience to the ben-fit of the customer.

We are very fortunate in Ireland to have such a wide variety of wines from round the world to offer the consumer, and that the time is now right to enjoy ine wines of the world in our restaurants.

The matching of wine and food is becoming as fascinating as the range of wine now available. While there are, however, a number of tried and tested combinations, here are a number of suggestions and guidelines. (In the end however it comes down to personal choice.)

Aperitifs:
Champagne is the best aperitif if money allows. Failing that, Australia's popula sparkler, Angas Brut, is a perfect alternative. A light refreshing Alsace like Pino Blanc, or Riesling, would also be ideal.

Pâté:
Light white for fish or vegetable-based; light medium-weight red for meat-based.

Smoked salmon:
Richly flavoured white (Gewürzträminer).

Shell fish:
Oysters, Mussels: firm, dry white (Muscadet Sur Lie, Chablis, Sancerre).
Prawns: dry white (Burgundy Bordeaux, New World Chardonnay).
Lobster: full flavoured white (Chablis ler Cru upwards to top white Burgundy)

Fish Dishes (type of sauce may alter choice):
Dry white, (Chardonnay or Sauvignon Blanc based).

Salmon:
Full rich white-top Burgundy or oak aged New World Chardonnay.

Chicken, turkey, guinea fowl:
Virtually any wine, red is most popularly used. (Red Bordeaux, Italian or any good Cabernet or Burgundy).

Chinese food:
Medium dry white (Chardonnay, Sauvignon Blanc) or alternatively medium to full red (Rhone wines, Cru Bourgeois claret).

Game birds:
Best quality reds you can afford.

Lamb:
Traditionally good red Bordeaux or New World Cabernet equivalent.

Pork:
Reasonably-full flavoured white (good Chardonnay, Rioja reds or Portugese, Italian).

Venison:
Strongest red (Barolo, Hermitage or young top quality Bordeaux).

Vegetarian:
Fennel, onion, leek based - Firm dry white Chardonnay, peppers, aubergines, spinach based - vigorous red, Italian or Rhone.

Cheese:
Only serve fine wines with mild cheese, very strong cheese masks the flavours of the wines.

Desserts:
Most sweet wines, here are some to look out for - Pacherenc de la St Albert, Muscat Beaumes de Venise or Rivesaltes, Sauternes, German Auslèse or better Moscato.

Courtesy of Nigel Werner
Findlater (Wine Merchants) Ltd.

Daytime

This is one of the largest sections in the guide and rightly so. Dublin city and county are crammed with little cafes, sandwich bars, coffee shops and self-service restaurants, which for various reasons choose to, or are obliged to, close by evening.

Many establishments appearing in this section are small premises servicing work or office environments in the commercial areas of the city. Some operate in busy shopping districts while others, like the Powerscourt Centre, still are tied to shopping centre hours of trading.

Breakfast in Dublin is becoming ever more popular. Watching the city come alive over a steaming mug of tea or a piping cup of freshly brewed coffee is a great way to start the day. Early risers can try the Mimosa Salad Bar (av £2.80) which opens at 7.30am. For those whose day starts a little later, there's the Mary Rose Restaurant in the Powerscourt Townhouse where everything, bar the sliced bread, is prepared on the premises to ensure freshness.

Many of these do a steaming trade during lunchtime, supplying their real raison d'être.

For those with a sweet tooth, afternoon tea or morning coffee is a great excuse to tuck in to delicious pastries, buns and gateaux. Most cafes/coffee shops/restaurants inlcude a wide range on their menu - your only problem will be choosing which ones to have!

Whether you're exhausted from a shopping spree, worn out from exploring the city, too lazy to cook, waiting for a friend, or just have an attack of the 'munchies', anytime from 8am-8pm, you'll find something in this section to suit your needs!

Marks Bros

7 South Great Georges Street, Dublin 2
Tel 6771085
Seating 80
Open 10am-5pm Mon-Sat; closed Sun
Average £3 soup and sandwich.
Payment LV

A student-oriented coffee/sandwich bar, close to the Georges Street/Dame Street traffic lights, brightly decorated with posters of rock music and film derivation.The menu here, chalked on the board behind the counter, has remained unchanged for at least five years! There is obviously no need as there is always a queue at lunchtime. There are always two soups - general vegetable and spinach - thick and tasty and almost a meal in themselves (extremely good value at 90p). Doorstep sandwiches (£1.50) are well filled, with a choice of avocado, salmon, tuna, cheese - and substantial salads, cauliflower and cheese, garlic mushrooms, pasta, coleslaw are all freshly made daily. Delicious carrot cake and apricot crunchies make for a good conclusion. Seating is provided on three levels and yet it still tends to get very busy at lunchtime. Bright and cheerful with a touch of the Latin quarter.

Babies/children allowed. No smoking area, (8).Takeaway. Ground floor. Stairs to ladies restroom and additional seating.

Phillers

14 Crown Alley, Temple Bar, Dublin 2
Tel 6711744
Seating 65
Open 7.30am-6pm Mon-Sat
Average £4, £1.50 minimum 12.30pm-2.30pm.
Unlicensed.
Payment LV

This sandwich bar/restaurant has a firm reputation founded on its cheesecakes. The menu features filled rolls, baps, triple-deckers, toasted sandwiches and salads. Lasagne and bolognese are served steaming hot in bowls. The system is that you place

your order, grab a seat and the food is brought down to you, which tends to work, but if things get hectic, you could be left stranded. However, this can be forgiven as the best in Phillers is kept to last - a choice of at least four or five different cheesecakes - large slices, fresh, creamy, brimming over with calories and absolute heaven for those with a fetish!
Babies/children catered for, child portions. Not really wheelchair friendly. No smoking area (26) Tables outdoors during summer. Takeaway. Ground floor one level.

Paddy Kavanagh's
6 Pembroke Row, Dublin 2
Tel 6765056
Seating 100
Open 7.30am-4pm Mon-Fri.
Average £7; £2.50 minimum noon-2pm; house wine £7.95, glass £1.55.
Payment TC.
Framed poems of Kavanagh upstairs and memorabilia on the walls lend a literary touch to brunching here. Very popular daytime restaurant for white collars in the locale. Run by an amicable Cavanman, food is steady with a jug of water on every table. Light, spacious and self-service.
Booking advisable. No smoking area (15). Tables outdoors (30). Takeaway and outdoor catering. Ground floor. First floor and stairs.

Wed Wose
18 Exchequer Street, Dublin 2
Tel none
Seating 70
Open 7am-7pm six days.
Average £5; £1.50 minimum 1pm-2pm.
Trucker-style cafe with bric-a-brac on walls, red brick counter and serviceable wooden tables and chairs. Regulars perch on high stools at the formica counter. Portions are adequate, menu inexpensive and it's somewhere you dress down, rather than up for. Speciality here is all day breakfast. Vegetarian available.
Babies/children catered for. Child menu and portions. Wheelchair friendly (except toilets). No smoking area (17). Takeaway. Private parties downstairs. Ground floor and basement. Stairs down to toilets.

Gerry's
6 Montague Street, Dublin 2
Tel 6783524
Seating 34
Open 7am-7pm Mon-Fri; 8am-2.30pm Sat.
Average £2.25 all day breakfast, lunch
Payment LV, TC
More cafe than "caff" with cottage-style seating, cloth covered tables and cooking just like mother's. Dishes include stuffed trout, roast beef and home-made pies including French apple and blackberry. Speciality again is all-day breakfast.
Babies/children catered for, child portions. No smoking area (8). Takeaway. Ground floor.

Applewoods
13 Lord Edward Street, Dublin 2
Tel 6799077
24 Dame Street Dublin 2
Tel6773353
Seating 12/50
Open 8.30am-5.30pm Mon-Sat; 10am-11.30pm Mon-Sat; both closed Sun
Average £11; house wine £8.50.
Payment A, V; EC, TC, LV.
This bistro, coffee and pastry shop started in tiny premises close to Christchurch. Its high ceiling, brightly painted walls and plain wooden furnishings help to create a quiet haven away from the hustle and bustle of this part of town. A nice feature worth remembering are the bunches of dried flowers hanging on the walls. Applewoods specialises in traditional food, vegetarian and provides a combination of beef, pasta and chicken dishes. Among the most interesting starters are black pudding with onions and apricots at £2.60 and a very good hummus. Bruschetta is an appetising starter or lunchtime snack. Main courses including beef, Italian pesto and a chicken liver dish are all around £5-6. The selection of desserts include a delicious bread and butter pudding, rhubarb tart and strawberries in

season, all under £2.
Babies/children allowed. No smoking area (15). Takeaway. Ground floor. Stairs.

The Refectory
2-4 Lord Edward Street, Dublin 2
Tel 6799643
Seating 70
Open 8.30am-8.30pm seven days
Average £7.50; £1.50 minimum 12.30pm-2.30pm; house wine £7.75, glass £1.50; £2.50 corkage per 750ml bottle.
Payment EC, TC
This restaurant capitalises very much on the Christchurch theme with paintings and pictures portraying the history of Christchurch adorning the walls. With Kinlay House (accommodation arm of USIT) just next door and "Dublinia" around the corner, the place is never short of a tourist. Even without the basement, there is a darkness to the Refectory - you could almost anticipate the appearance of a brother in medieval garb addressing you in Latin as you attack your Irish breakfast for £2. One of the very few places in Dublin to serve schnitzel (£5.50).
Babies/children catered for, child portions. No smoking area (17). Toilets in Kinlay house . Booking advisable. Air conditioned. Private parties catered for. Takeaway. Neat casual dress. Ground floor . Basement and stairs.

Zebras
9 Harcourt Road, Dublin 2
Tel 4780707
Seating 14
Open 7.30am-6pm Mon-Fri.
Payment TC, LV
A salad/sandwich bar with a black/white decor hence its name that specialises in sandwiches to suit all tastes. Vegetarians are catered for as well.
Babies/children catered for, child portions. Wheelchair friendly except toilets. Takeaway and delivery to offices outside the immediate locality.

Tasty Options
112 Lower Dorset Street, Dublin 1
Tel 302857
Seating 28
Open 7.30am-6pm Mon-Sat; closed Sun
Average £5.90; house wine per glass £1.85.
Payment EC
A salad/snack bar in a busy location. This clean airy eatery is distinguished by art deco decor, light wood floors, black tables and stools, and looks rather out of place beside a launderette in Dorset Street. There is a selection of snacks, sandwiches and rolls along with dependables like quiche and pizza which are served all day.
Babies/children catered for, child portions. Not really wheelchair friendly. No smoking 12.30pm-2pm. Takeaway. Ground floor.

Sambos
4 Lombard Street East, Dublin 2
Tel 671353
Seating 20
Open 8am-4.30pm Mon-Fri; closed Sat/Sun
Average £2.95 sandwich, coffee and cheesecake.
A sandwich bar just a short hop away from Pearse Street station with a fine selection of homemade soups that changes daily but includes potato and leek and carrot and tomato. The BLT sandwich and cheesecake come highly recommended and are strong contenders on a varied menu.
Babies/children allowed. No smoking area (6). Takeaway. Ground floor.

The Niche
26 Dawson Street, Dublin 2
Tel 6776693
Seating 18
Open 8am-6pm Mon-Fri
Average house wine glass £1.95
Payment EC, LV
This pert little sandwich bar serves a variety of light snacks with wine by the glass. A genial hostess ensures good service.
Babies/children allowed. Takeaway .

Flanagans Coffee Shop
Unit 10, Castle House, South Great Georges Street, Dublin 2
Tel 4750225
Seating 44
Open 7.30am-5.30pm
Average £2.95 hot lunch; 95p-£2. breakfast; house wine 1/4 bottle £2.
Payment LV
A sandwich bar whose address might be confusing but is opposite Bewley's. The reasonably priced breakfast is really worth going out of your way for but so is the lunch special £2.50, for soup, sandwich and coffee. A suitable venue for the shopper/traveller on a strict budget.
Babies/children catered for, child portions. No smoking area (8). Takeaway. Ground floor.

Subs & Salads
14 South Anne Street, Dublin 2
Tel 6798847
Seating 16
Open 9am-5pm Mon-Sat
Average £1.15 sandwich; £1.70 bap; £1.80 sub; £1.80 breakfast till noon.
Payment LV
This eatery supplies an ample array of good value sandwiches and subs. Lots of stars for good value.
Babies/children allowed. Wheelchair friendly (except toilets). No smoking area (3). Takeaway. Ground floor..

The Drop In
1 St. Mary's Terrace, Dalkey, Co Dublin
Tel none
Open 11am-3pm
Average £2.50 lunch main course
This snack bar used to be a wine bar and between 7pm-10pm doubles as a youth centre, an alternative to pubs and also an ideal spot to leave children whilst dining in one or other of Dalkey's five restaurants. Aside from a comfortable setting for a reasonably priced lunch, do try their pancakes!

Rooftop Restaurant / Coffee Shop / Tearooms
Clery's Department Store
18-27 O'Connell Street, Dublin 1
Tel 87286000
Seating 160; 140; 80
Open 9am-5pm
Average £3.95 carvery; £6.95 carvery rooftop; house wine £7.70, 1/4 litre £1.85.
Payment A, AmEx, V; EC, TC, LV. Service charge optional
Three restaurants - basement coffee shop, tearooms with waitress service, self-service rooftop - bright, cheerful and pleasant.
Babies/children catered for, child portions and menu; high chairs and in-store crêche. No smoking area (80); (70); (40). Private parties catered for in tea rooms. Three levels. Stairs. Lift.

Graham O'Sullivan
12 Duke Street, Dublin 2
Tel 6775612 .
Seating 100
28 South Anne Street, Dublin 2
Tel 6777340
Dun Laoghaire Shopping Centre
Tel 2801960/2800027
Artane Shopping Centre
Tel 310789
Northside Shopping Centre
Tel 8484103

The Fountain Restaurant
Shopping Centre, Blackrock, Co. Dublin
Tel 2836855
Seating 90
Open 9am-6pm Mon-Wed/Sat; 9am-9pm Thurs Fri; closed Sun
Average £5; dishes from £2.35; house wine £6.95; 1/4 bottle £2.15. Payment A, V; EC, TC, LV
Self-service restaurant specialising in fresh food cooked on the premises. A good place for a snack and a coffee while shopping. They even do 'espresso coffee'. Full breakfast at £2.65 consists of orange juice, full fry-up, toast and coffee while a mini breakfast at £1.50 will get you a fry and coffee.

Babies/children catered for, child portions and menu; high chairs. No smoking area (30). Tables outdoors. Takeaway. Ground floor.

Dinty Moore's
21 D'Olier Street, Dublin 2
Tel 6712072
Seating 72
Open 8am-6.30pm Mon-Sat; closed Sun.
Average £5.20. Unlicensed.
Payment LV
This self-service restaurant is bustling and busy at lunch time. Its gigantic portions are much favoured by students and office workers who generally prefer to have their main meal in the middle of the day. The green walls and bamboo blinds give the impression of some exotic tropical spot. The Irish stew at £3.45 as well as being plentiful is very comforting on a wet afternoon. Other dishes include hamburgers (the chef's speciality) and bacon, cabbage and potatoes. Star dessert is lemon cheesecake but the cappuccino (on this occasion at any rate) was unfortunately from a packet. A touch of the Irish, which should appeal to the visitor.
Babies/children catered for, child portions and menu. No smoking area (25). Air conditioned. Ground floor.

Woods
111/112 Lower Baggot Street, Dublin 2
Tel 6611806
Seating 50
Open 7.30am-6.30pm Mon-Fri,; 8.30am-4.00pm Sat; closed Sun.
Average £5.50; £1.50 minimum noon-2pm; £3 smaller lunch; house wine £6.95, ¼ bottle £1.69.
Payment LV
This two tiered self-service restaurant favours home-cooked food and Saturday breakfast. Breakfast is served from 7.30am-11am and lunch from noon until closing at 6.30pm. The area is very business oriented - meetings take place and colleagues chat over breakfast. The self-service counter is attractive, the food appealing to the eye. Offering value for money, it is clean and comfortable and gives the option of a table on the pavement.

Babies/children catered for, child portions. No smoking area (16). Tables outdoors. Takeaway. Ground floor. Stairs.

Figaro's
above Acquiesce, 41 Grafton Street, Dublin 2
Tel 6719795
Seating 60
Open 9.30am-5.30pm Mon-Sat; closed Sun
Average £3-6; house wine £10, glass £1.80.
Payment TC, LV
This self-service restaurant boasts affordable prices for good food and afternoon teas as well as catering for vegetarians. It is a newly opened concept restaurant, put together by the owners of the 'Dome'. The decor and food are similar but without the spectacular view overlooking Stephen's Green.
Babies/children catered for, child portions, high chairs. Not wheelchair friendly. No smoking area (12). Stairs.

Gray's
Celtic Court, 109D Lower Baggot Street, Dublin 2
Tel 6760676
Seating 70
Open 7.30am-6pm Mon-Fri; closed Sat/Sun
Average £6.70; ££2.50 minimum12.30pm-1.30pm; house wine £7.95.
Payment A, V; EC, TC, LV
A self-service restaurant offering occasional entertainment and home-cooked food but not vegetarian. Winner of a Bewley's Coffee Award, it is the only self-service restaurant in Dublin serving cafetière coffee. It is situated in a converted coach house whose original stone has been retained, upstairs Ronnie Leahy paintings are exhibited, with Owen Walshe's exhibited downstairs.
Babies/children catered for, child portions. Not wheelchair friendly. No smoking area (12/14). Booking advisable. Tables outdoors. Private room for parties for 60/70. Takeaway. Ground floor and upstairs.

Shelley's Restaurant
35 North Frederick Street, Dublin 1
Tel 8724200
Seating 50
Open 8am-7pm seven days
Average £4.50 lunch; £6.95 dinner; £1.50 minimum; £2.45 full breakfast, £1,50 mini breakfast
A nice looking self-service restaurant/salad bar specialising in breakfast, four-course lunches and toasted bacon sandwiches. Vegetarians are also catered for. Clean and functional with tables on the street, it offers good value for money. Service is speedy, making it an ideal spot if you are in a hurry.
Babies/children catered for, child portions and special menu. Wheelchair friendly (except toilets). No smoking area (16). Takeaway.

Galligans
6 Merrion Row, Dublin 2
Tel 6765955
Seating 100
Open 7.30am-7pm Mon-Fri; 9am-5pm Sat/Sun.
Average £5-6; £2 minimum 12.30pm-2pm; £2.95 main course; house wine £7.95.
Payment all major credit cards EC,TC, LV
A self service restaurant specialising in lasagne, salads and homemade pastries. Vegetarian available.
Babies/children catered for, child portions. Not wheelchair friendly. No smoking area (26-30). Takeaway. Ground floor. Basement and stairs down.

Kingfisher Restaurant
166 Parnell Street, Dublin 1
Tel 8728732
Seating 50
Open 8am-8pm Mon-Sat; till 9pm Thurs; 10am-7.30pm Sun
Average £4.50; £2.25 breakfast; house wine ½ bottle £4.95.
Payment all major credit cards except AmEx; LV, TC.
A budget restaurant that looks like a fish and chip shop. It lays claim to 98FM Radio's 1990 Award for Dublin's best breakfast, consisting of bacon, egg, sausage, mushrooms, beans, tomato and black pudding only £2.25. A champagne breakfast of smoked salmon, brown bread and a bottle of Veuve de Vernay

comes out at £9 per head. At £4.95, the house wine must be the cheapest in Dublin. Specialities include fresh fish and homemade chips.
Babies/children catered for; high chairs and baby changing room. No smoking area (20). Tables outdoors and private parties catered for when restaurant closes. Takeaway. Ground floor. Stairs.

The Garden Bistro
16 Parnell Square, Dublin 1
Tel 8740806
Seating 40
Open 9am-7pm Mon-Sat; 9pm-6pm Sun
Average £4.95 (up to 7pm); £3.95 lunch 12.30pm-2pm; house wine glass £1.50.
Payment LV.
Cheerful with red oil cloth on all tables, the Garden Bistro caters for the budget-conscious with a selection from a continental breakfast at 65p, butties and tea or coffee for £1, a fry up at £2 to a fry with cereal or porridge at £2.50.
Babies/children catered for, child portions and menu; baby changing room. Not wheelchair friendly. No smoking area (8). Tables outdoors. Takeaway. Ground floor. Stairs.

Purdy's Pantry
Serpentine Court, Serpentine Avenue, Ballsbridge, Dublin 4
Tel 6605049
Seating 30
Open 8am-5pm Mon-Fri; 8am-3.30pm Sat.
Average £3.50; £1.20 desserts; £2 minimum.
Small self-service restaurant with home-cooked foods and bakery attached. Located next to DART crossing at Serpentine Avenue.
Babies/children allowed. Not wheelchair friendly. No smoking area (10). Tables outdoors. Takeaway

Weir's Restaurant
1A Beatty's Avenue, Ballsbridge, Dublin 4
Tel 6682810
Seating 35
Open 7.30 am - 5.30 pm Mon-Fri; closed weekend
Average about £4 lunch; £2-3.50 breakfast 7.30am-11 am; house wine £8, glass £1.78
Payment TC, LV.
In a very nice location down a side street in Ballsbridge and close to Jurys and the Berkeley Court Hotels, as well as the RDS. There are seats outside so you can join the cafe society. Breakfasts are the speciality with black puddings coming all the way from Kerry. Lunches, all homemade, include chicken and potato cakes as well as lasagne and quiche.
Babies/children catered for, child portions. No smoking area (12). Tables outdoors, Takeaway. Ground floor.

Chewy's
Merrion Centre, Nutley Lane/Merrion Road, Dublin 4
Telephone 2838409
Seating 68
Open 9am-7pm Mon-Wed; 9am-9pm Thurs/Fri; 9am-6pm Sat; closed Sun.
Average £4.95; £1.75 minimum 12,30pm-1.45pm; house wine 1/4 bottle £2.20.
A favourite lunch spot for those working in nearby St Vincent's Hospital, embassies and RTE, not to mention shoppers in the supermarket. This is an excellent spot for breakfast before launching into the weekend shopping. Friendly service in the Merrion Centre.

Kilkenny Kitchen
Kilkenny Shop, 6 Nassau Street, Dublin 2
Tel 677706
Seating 170
Open 9am-5pm Mon-Sat
Average under £7; £2 minimum 12.30pm-2.30pm; £2 breakfast up to 11am, house wine 1/2 bottle £4.50, 1/4 bottle £2.
Payment all major credit cards
The Kilkenny Shop is known for the wide range of Irish goods it stocks. Tour operators bring busloads of visitors here so they can bring back home 'a little bit of Ireland'. Upstairs, before or after making all those purchases, the Kilkenny Kitchen is buzzing. It is a self-service restaurant where the emphasis

is on traditional Irish home cooking. Specialities include - cold meats and fish, but also available are coddle, Irish stew and boiled beef and cabbage. Soup and interesing sandwiches are tasty alternatives. A selection of jams, chutneys, biscuits and other goodies are edible souvenirs of a visit.
Babies/children catered for, child portions, high chairs and baby changing room. Not wheelchair friendly.

Chompy's Deli Restaurant
1st Floor, Powerscourt Townhouse, South William Street, Dublin 2
Tel 6794552
Seating 150
Open 8am-6pm Mon-Sat; closed Sun.
Average £6.50; house wine £9, glass £1.50.
Payment A, V; EC, TC, LV - anything but roubles!
Welcome to the Susie and Frankie show! A delightful story of fortysomething amorous abandon (full story posted outside restaurant) and a real desire for decent bagels led to its opening. It is the recreation of the New York deli in Dublin's poshest centre with full American breakfast - pancakes with maple syrup (£2), eggs benedict (£2.20) and bagels (£1-4). The menu is an amusement in itself, written as it is in word play - try 'the spice who loved me' (£4.80) or 'whistle a happy tuna' (£3.55) and decide for yourself if you are paying extra for the designer name. Children are particularly well catered for with substantial Häagen-Dazs offerings .. or should I say adults? Significant applause for unlimited tea/coffee refills.
Babies/children catered for, child portions; high chairs. Not wheelchair friendly. No smoking area (24). Tables outdoors. First floor. Stairs.

Corries Kitchen
31 Lower Baggot Street, Dublin 2
Tel 6768103
Seating 26
Open 7.30 am-6pm Mon-Fri; 10.30am-6pm Sat; closed Sun.
Average £6; £3.85 main course; house wine 1/4 litre £2.50; tea/coffee refills free.
Payment TC
Corries Kitchen has replaced Sheares Restaurant and, at the time of writing, was still finding its feet. This basement cafe, with a black and white tiled floor and peach walls, is intimate if not claustrophobic. Family-run, it gives a service that is cosy and informal. Very keen to highlight their Robert Roberts coffee, the wine (1/4 bottles only), however, is quite expensive. Worthy breakfast with a smile.
Not wheelchair friendly. No smoking are (6). Booking advisable. Takeaway. Basement.

Maxwells
35 Parliament Street, Dublin 2
Tel 6718618
Seating 52
Open 8am-6pm Mon-Fri; 10am-4pm Sat.
Average £5.40. Unlicensed.
Payment A, V; EC, TC, LV.
Located in what was a fringe niche in central Dublin, fortune and rapid development have now drawn Parliament Street into the throbbing arena of Temple Bar. Maxwells

has benefitted as a daytime self-service cafe with homecooked foods in more than adequate quantities at prices that would make it economically unviable to pack your own lunch. It has thus built a strong regular trade. Unexceptional decor allows you to concentrate on the food in hand.
Babies/children catered for, child portions. Not wheelchair friendly. No smoking area (17). Tables outdoors. Private room for parties after 6pm. Takeaway. Ground floor. Basement and stairs down.

The Livingroom
20 Lincoln Place, Dublin 2
Tel 6761893
Seating 60
Open 9am-8pm Mon-Fri; 10.30 am-4pm Sat; closed Sun.
Average £6.35; £2 minimum 12.30pm-2pm; £3.95 meat dish including baked potato and two salads; £3.65 vegetarian dishes; house wine £7.95.
Payment LV
Bernie's Kitchen or her 'Living Room' is just about the most over-populated in all Dublin - and for good reason. She has even had to extend downstairs to cater for what is about the worst-kept secret in the city centre ... but could you ever trust a Trinity student? Excellent, well-priced food with at least two vegetarian options per day make this eatery a constantly busy thoroughfare for business people and students alike. Main courses at £3-4 are generous and you will not see your partner over the desserts. Even though it is self-service, staff are ever helpful and eager to please.
Babies/children allowed. No smoking area (20). Booking advisable. Tables outdoors. Takeaway. Ground floor. Basement and stairs down.

Alpha Restaurant
Corner Wicklow Street/ Clarendon Street, Dublin 2.
Tel 6770213
Seating 50
Open 10am-7pm Mon-Fri; 10am-3pm Sat
Average £3.75; £3.55 two course lunch; £3.95 four courses; £1.95 afternoon tea 3pm-6pm

A small, rather old-fashioned upstairs cafe with formica tables, where the fare ranges from grilled steak and chips to egg on toast. The very reasonably priced two-course lunch comprises a main course such as fried fillet of cod, shepherd's pie or roast beef and the menu changes daily. All in all great value. A favourite haunt of students from nearby Trinity College.
Babies/children catered for. Not wheelchair friendly. No smoking area (12). Private room for parties. Takeaway. Stairs.

The Dome Restaurant
2nd Floor, St Stephen's Green Centre, Dublin 2
Tel 4781287
Seating 120
Open 9am-5.30pm Mon-Sat; closed Sun
Average £5; £4.50 afternoon tea; house wine £8.50, glass £1.80.
Payment LV
The Dome, at the top of the Stephen's Green Centre, is big, bright and cosy - perhaps the closest Dublin can come to an Italian open air cafe. To allow for the vagaries of the weather, it is entirely glassed in. The view over Stephen's Green is stunning and it would be wonderful at night! A special venue for lunch, an important meeting, afternoon tea and to complete the experience, live music. Not to be missed. Specialities include pork steak Wellington and afternoon tea with wonderful cakes. Vegetarian options are also available.
Babies/children catered for, child portions; high chairs and baby changing room. No smoking area (16). Stairs. Lift.

Restaurant Mahler
Powerscourt Townhouse, South William Street, Dublin 2
Tel 6797117
Seating 60
Open 9am-5.30pm Mon-Sat; closed Sun
Average £2.45 breakfast; £6.50 lunch; house wine £8.95, glass £1.85.
Payment A, V; EC, LV
Daytime restaurant in the basement of this popular shopping complex. Yellow walls, pine floor and pine topped tables give it a clean, scrubbed look and in keeping with its name, taped classical music is played at lunchtime. Self-service lunch offers four dishes: a joint, a casserole, a vegetarian dish and perhaps a bake or fish dish with sensible portions. Verdict: a civilised place to eat.
Babies/children catered for, child portions. Not wheelchair friendly. No smoking area (40). Booking advisable for parties. Tables outdoors. Private parties catered for at night. Takeaway. Stairs.

Mary Rose Restaurant
Powerscourt Centre, South William Street, Dublin 2
Tel 6794160
Seating 92
Open 9am-5.30pm Mon-Fri; 8.30am-5.30pm Sat
Average £4; £1.99 breakfast . Unlicensed
Payment TC, LV
This restaurant is in the middle of the Powerscourt Centre where everything is made on the premises - only sliced bread is brought in. The array of cakes is wonderful! Breakfast is available weekdays from 9 and on Saturday from 8.30. Lunch all day can be breast of chicken on a bed of garlic potato, with a small side-salad. Vegetarians are catered for. Although Mary Rose's is a self service, staff go out of their way to seat and make the customer happy. By the way, the Irish soccer team call in here on the eve of a match.
Babies/children catered for, child portions; high chairs and baby changing room. No smoking area (31). Takeaway. Ground floor. Stairs.

Juggy's Well
3 Glasthule Road, Sandycove, Co Dublin
Tel 2806217
Seating 48
Open 10am-6pm Mon-Sat; closed Sun
Average £6.90; house wine (Cuvée) 1/4 litre £1.95
Juggy's Well, which takes its name from an old well behind the Old Monkstown Hospital, was an old private dwelling knocked to a shell. The basement was raised, first floor

taken out and a timber staircase inserted. The self-service counter is almost an intrusion into an otherwise very homely setting of pale sunlight-yellow walls and black and white tiling which also suggest absolute spotlessness. The stairwell and second floor are carpeted to create a different effect. Everything on the menu including soups, quiches, lasagne, curried chicken - is cooked on the premises by Nell Fitzgerald and family who offer value for money in comfortable no-nonsense surroundings.
Babies/children catered for. No smoking area (24 downstairs). Restaurant available for private parties of 40/50. Takeaway by arrangement. Ground floor. Mezzanine and stairs.

Mary Anne's Kitchen
54 Mary Street, Dublin 1
Tel 8723680
Seating 50
Open 8.30am-5.30pm Mon-Sat; closed Sun
Average £2.20 breakfast; £3.50 dinner; £2.50 soup and sandwich.
This plain, friendly family-oriented lunch/diner is run by a mother and son team. Soups are vegetarian in content, so expect minestrone or mushroom. Sandwich fillings are fairly typical of a diner of this sort.
Babies/children catered for, child portions and menu. No smoking area (15). Takeaway. Ground floor. Stairs

Piglet's
4 The Mews, Monkstown Crescent, Monkstown
Tel none
Seating n/a
Open 10am-5pm Tues-Sat
Average £1 coffee and scone; £2.30-3 lunch. Unlicensed
This coffee shop, snack bar with a piglet motif throughout, serves home-made cakes and pastries. Specialities are carrot cake and brown bread.

Continental Coffee Shop
8 Main Street, Dundrum, Dublin 14
Tel 2989599
Seating 24
Open 9am-6pm Mon-Sat
Average lunch from £1.50. Unlicensed
Payment LV
Attached to a bakery, it is ideal for breakfast for which you can expect to pay about £1.65. Cakes and pastries make it a good venue for morning coffee or afternoon tea. Set price meals are also available.
Babies/children welcome. Not wheelchair friendly. No smoking (12). Takeaway. Stairs.

The Pastry Case Bakery & Coffee Shop
312 Lower Rathmines Road, Rathmines, Dublin 6
Tel 975660
Seating 36
Open 9am-6pm Mon-Sat
Average £1.99 breakfast all day; main dish about £1.50. Unlicensed.
Payment LV. Service charge at customer's discretion.

A trendy little cafe, just opposite Quinnsworth and beside the Swan Centre in the heart of Rathmines. The lunchtime special of pizza and side salad or baked potato is good value at £2, as is the breakfast of two sausages, bacon, egg, tomato, toast and tea or coffee. Specialities include fresh baked French breads and breakfasts and vegetarians are catered for.
Babies/children allowed. Not wheelchair friendly. No smoking area (16). Takeaway. Ground floor. Stairs.

The Coffee Bean
7 Anglesey Building, Georges Street, Dun Laoghaire, Co Dublin
Tel 2809522
Seating 60
Open 8am-5pm Mon-Sat; open Sun in summer.
Average £2.45 full Irish breakfast 8am-noon; £3.30 lunch. Unlicensed.
This coffee shop and restaurant, offers a variety of sandwiches, baps, 'wonderful' coleslaw and for complete indulgence, Häagen-Dazs ice-cream is also available.
Babies/children catered for, child menu; high chairs. No smoking area defined. Takeaway.

Relish Delicatessen
70 Upper Georges Street, Dun Laoghaire, Co Dublin
Tel 2809713
Seating 40
Open 9am-5.30pm Mon-Sat
Average £2 baps; non-alcoholic wine 1/4 bottle £1.85
Coffee shop selling home-baked rolls, delicious and enormous filled baps and French sticks. Bread baked to an old Irish recipe. Well worth a visit.
Babies/children catered for, child portions. Not wheelchair friendly. No smoking area (15). Takeaway. Stairs.

Coffee Garden
Shopping Centre, Dun Laoghaire, Co Dublin
Tel none
Seating 60
Open shopping hours
Average £2.50
Standard shopping centre snack bar, providing light refreshment for busy shoppers as well as vegetarian options.
Babies/children catered for. Not wheelchair friendly.

Nicky's Coffee Shop
Shopping Cetre, Dun Laoghaire, Co Dublin
Tel 2802182
Seating 35
Open 8.30am-5.30pm Mon-Sat; 8.30am-9.30pm Fri.
Average £1.10 sandwich
Snack bar serving probably the best coffee in Dun Laoghaire. Its menu includes tea, cakes, sandwiches and usual cafe fare.
Babies/children allowed. No smoking area (3). Takeaway. Ground floor.

The Buzz Cafe
40 Main Street, Blackrock, Co Dublin
Tel 2883854
Seating 34
Open 10am-6pm seven days
Average £4 main course and coffee; £2.90 minimum all day. Unlicensed.
This cafe/eatery boasts the best coffee in Blackrock with a cosmopolitan flavour! Photographers exhibit their work here, giving it an 'arty' feel.
Babies/children catered for, child portions. Takeaway. Ground floor.

Pavlova Pantry
Top Floor, Stephen's Green Shopping Centre, Dublin 2
Tel 4784114
Seating 54
Open 8am - 6.30pm Mon-Sat
Average £7.50; house wine 1/4 bottle £1.95
Payment LV
No guesses for the speciality. Yes - it's Pavlova which Mary Curran learned to make in the Home of Pavlova - Australia. In this busy little coffee shop/restaurant on the top floor of the Stephen's Green Centre, traditional or jumbo breakfast is available until 11am and lunch dishes include reliables

like quiche and lasagne with a chicken dish of some kind. Sit in the smoking area for a French cafe atmosphere and enjoy the view down into the heart of the centre. It's the first of its kind in Dublin to win a Bewleys Award for Service and Coffee.
Babies/children catered for, child portions and menu. No smoking area (26). Takeaway. Stairs.

Cunningham's Coffee Shop
35a Kildare Street, Dublin 2
Tel 6762952
Seating 18
Open 9am- 5pm Mon-Fri
Average £5.50; £2 minimum at discretion ; house wine small bottles.
Payment TC
This coffee shop/sandwich bar, where almost all the seats are non-smoking, displays a photograph of itself taken in 1922. Filtered coffee is available.
Babies/children catered for, child portions. Not wheelchair friendly. Takeaway. Ground floor.

Sherry's Delicatessan and Coffee Shop
55 Ranelagh, Dublin 6
Tel 963863
Seating 34
Open 8am-7pm Mon-Fri; 8.30am-7pm Sat; 11am-7pm Sun
Average £3.85 main course; £2.75 breakfast fry-up.
Payment TC, LV
A little place with the air of a trattoria specialising in sandwiches and baps with unusual fillings, like blue cheese and pineapple and chicken with asparagus and salad. Their all day breakfast makes Sherry's different. Although the breads are not gluten- free, their salads are fine for coeliacs and there is also a wide range of vegetarian dishes
Babies/children catered for, child portions and menu; high chairs. No smoking area (10). Takeaway. Ground floor. Stairs to toilets.

Chavalee's Cafe
5 George's Avenue, Blackrock, Co. Dublin.
Tel 2882250
Seating 64
Open 8am-6pm Mon-Sat.
Average £5 main course and dessert; 99p light breakfast; house wine 1/2 litre carafe £4.50, glass £1.60.
Payment TC, LV
A little French-style cafe tucked away off Blackrock's main street specialises in home-cooked food with vegetarian options. You can browse through the newspapers as you enjoy a light breakfast of scone or croissant and tea/coffee which is available up to 11am - surely the best value in town.
Babies/children catered for, child portions. No smoking area (28). Takeaway. Ground floor.

Beggar's Banquet
Unit 1, Chatham Court, Chatham Street, Dublin 2
Tel 6716861
Seating 18
Open 7.30am-5pm Mon-Sat; closed Sun
Average £2.95; £1.99 mini breakfast; £1.50 minimum 12.30pm-2pm. Unlicensed.
The Beggar's Banquet, on the site of an old greasy spoon, has now become a smart snack/lunch bar. The mini-breakfast of bacon, egg, sausage, tea or coffee and orange juice is popular as are their hot lunches. They also do packed lunches at under £10 for four. Vegetarian options are available.
Babies/children catered for, child portions. Tables outdoors. Takeaway and delivery. Ground floor. Stairs.

Leinster Coffee House
17 South Leinster Street, Dublin 2
Tel 6764356
Seating 25
Open 8am-8pm Mon-Sat; 9am-7pm Sun
Average £1.80 sandwich and coffee.
Payment A, V; EC, TC, LV
Modelled on a French/Italian style cafe bar, the coffee is delicious. A drinkable espresso in Dublin is a rare treat. Sandwiches are made to order.

Babies/children catered for; high chairs. No smoking area (19). Sandwich takeaway, delivery. Ground floor. Stairs to toilets.

Frederick's Restaurant
22 Frederick Street South, Dublin 2
Tel 6778288
Seating 60
Open 7.30am-5.30pm Mon-Fri; 10am-5pm Sat; closed Sun
Average £2 lunch; £1.50 minimum 12.30pm-2pm; house wine 1/4 bottle £2.25.
Payment LV
Frederick's claim that everything they do is homemade. The sandwich fillings include salmon and Emmental, BLT, crab and avocado, chicken, lemon and garlic. A hot dish of the day with two salads costs £3.25. Those with a sweet tooth can enjoy 'goodies' like cheesecake, carrot cake and pastries.
Babies/children allowed. No smoking area (25). Tables outdoors Private parties catered for night only. Takeaway, delivery. Ground floor. Stairs.

The Pantry
Unit 3, Store Street, Dublin 1
Tel 365334
Seating 32
Open 7.30am-6pm Mon-Sat; closed Sun
Average £2.95 main course; £2 breakfast.
Payment LV
Close to the central bus station (Busáras) and Connolly railway station, so well situated for the traveller, this cafe has an extensive menu that includes vegetarian options and wholesome fare at very reasonable prices! Lasagne and chips will cost £2.95 or a quarter pounder and chips, £2.40. Arthur Moore is a friendly man and if you need breakfast before catching the ferry, his should keep you going to Holyhead and beyond.
Babies/children catered for, child portions and menu. No smoking area (6) Takeaway. Ground floor. Stairs to toilets.

The Penny Farthing
30 Exchequer Street, Dublin 2
Tel 6772374
Seating 50
Open 7.30am-7pm Mon-Sat
Average £1.75-2.85 main dish; £1.60 breakfast all day.
Payment LV
A cottage-style cafe that is popular with the business community.
Babies/children catered for, child portions. Not wheelchair friendly. No smoking area (20). Takeaway. Ground floor.

Dimples Coffee Shop
32 Eden Quay, Dublin 1
Tel 8749478
Seating 18
Open 7.30am-7pm Mon-Sat; closed Sun.
Average £1.60 sandwich and coffee. Unlicensed
Dimples specialises in chicken, ham amd tuna sandwiches. Situated on Eden Quay, it is close not only to the Liffey but to O'Connell Street, the financial area and Busáras. Large baguette type sandwiches and instant coffee are served by attentive host Peter Dineen, one-time football pools winner!
Babies/children allowed. Takeaway. Ground floor.

The Village Coffee Shop & Wine Bar
54 Main Street, Swords, Co Dublin
Tel 8403951
Seating 40
Open 9am-6pm Mon-Sat
Average £6; £2.50 breakfast; £2.50 roll, soup and coffee; house wine £6.99.
Payment A, V; EC
Specialities here are lasagne and steak pie. Vegetarian options are also available. I can recommend a huge ham sandwich and a generous portion of salad, accompanied by a steaming bowl of homemade soup full of vegetables. The lunch special includes a cup of coffee and a chicken and mushroom pie with salad and chips for only £2.50.
Babies/children catered for, child portions and menu. Wheelchair friendly (except toilets). No smoking area (8).Tables outdoors. Restaurant available at night for private parties. Takeaway. Ground floor.

Costa Coffee Boutique
New Street Mall, Malahide, Co Dublin
Tel 8453060
Seating 20
Open 8.15am-5.30pm Mon-Sat; 11am-6pm Sun and bank hol
Unlicensed.
Costa Coffee, a UK franchise, has been setting its own standards in Dublin. Specialising in good coffee, the shops are found principally in stations and airports, although there is another outlet in the Westbury Mall. As well as coffee, they serve snacks they call 'gap fillers' - a toasted cheese and tomato sandwich or perhaps a light salad with brown bread. Desserts, a selection of 'sweeties', are available as well as a full range of tea and healthy cold drinks.
Babies/children allowed. No smoking area (6). Takeaway. Ground floor.

'51' Cafe and Deli
51 Ranelagh Village, Dublin 6
Tel 961759
Seating 30
Open 7am-8pm Mon-Thurs; -6pm Fri-Sun
Average £5. Unlicensed
This coffee shop serves good salads and vegetarian dishes are available. A busy place, they clearly have what people want. The proprietor claims it is his salads but breakfasts here are pretty good too.
Babies/children catered for, child portions and menu. Wheelchair friendly (except toilets). No smoking area (2). Takeaway. Ground floor.

The Coffee Deck
1 Lower Rathmines Road, Dublin 6
Tel 974246
Seating 28
Open 8am-6pm Mon-Fri; 9.30am-6pm Sat; 10.30am-6pm Sun
Average £3; £2.35 breakfast; £1.80 minimum noon-2pm. Unlicensed.
This brand new coffee shop is just a skip away from the Grand Canal and Portobello Bridge and specialises in salads. It is an airy spot, a good place to have breakfast and watch the world go by.
Babies/children catered for, child portions. Wheelchair friendly (except toilets). No smoking area (8). Takeaway. Ground floor.

Chimes
Unit 40, Swan Centre, Rathmines, Dublin 6.
Tel 963803
Seating 110
Open 8.30am-6.30pm Mon-Wed; 8.30-9pm Thurs/Fri; 8.30am-6pm Sat
Average £3.99; £2.99 main course; house wine £8.95, glass £1.40.
Payment LV
A coffee shop with restaurant upstairs which takes its name from the clock centrepiece within this shopping complex. The clock chimes every 15 minutes which to some may be attractive, to others annoying. The food is what you would expect in an eating place of this type. The speciality is banoffi and if you have never tried this delicious banana and toffee pudding, you're in for a treat.
Babies/children catered for, child portions and menu; high chairs and baby changing room. No smoking area (15). Stairs. Lift.

Keepers Restaurant
71 Mespil Road, Dublin 4
Tel 6605205
Seating 40
Open 8am-4pm Mon-Fri; closed Sat/Sun.
Average £5.95 lunch; £2.75 breakfast. Unlicensed.
Payment TC, LV.
This coffee shop has as its specialities quiche and lasagne, also caters for vegetarians and offers a pleasant and discreet venue for breakfast, morning meetings and lunches. Its 'raison d'être' is to serve the local business community but the Keeper, beside the Canal, is also a nice stop during a stroll along the towpath.
Babies/children catered for, child portions. Not wheelchair friendly. No smoking area (8). Takeaway. Stairs.

Cafe Kylemore
101 O'Connell Street, Dublin 1
Tel 8722138
Seating 200
St Stephen's Green Shopping Centre, Dublin 2
Tel 4781657.
Seating 400
Swan Centre, Rathmines, Dublin 6
Tel 966789
Seating 200
Open 8am-9pm Mon-Sat, noon-8pm Sun O'Connell Street; 8am-6pm Mon-Wed & Fri/Sat; - 8pm Thurs St Stephen's Green Centre; 8am-6pm Mon-Wed/Sat, 8am-9pm Thurs/Fri, closed Sun Rathmines Centre.
Average £4-5; £2.99 main course, dessert, coffee/tea noon-3pm, £1.99 full breakfast; house wine 1/4 bottle £2.50.
Payment EC, LV
Cafes specialising in lasagne, garlic bread, beef strogonoff, stir fries and salads, while catering for vegetarians. The Kylemore Bakery is over 200 years old and has over 50 shops countrywide.
Babies/children catered for, child menu (burger/sausage, beans and chips £1.50); high chairs and baby changing room in St Stephen's Green Centre. No smoking area (100). Ground floor. St Stephen's Green two levels. Stairs down to toilets. Lift St Stephen's Green only.

The Dorset
87 Upper Dorset Street, Dublin 7
Tel 306710
Seating 14
Open 6.30am-6pm Mon-Fri; 9am-6pm Sat; closed Sun
Average £2 breakfast; £2.75 bigger breakfast.
A cafe with a good value breakfast, also accommodating the vegetarian taste.
Babies/children catered for, child portions. Wheelchair friendly (except toilets). No smoking area (4). Takeaway. Ground floor.

Priscilla's
New Street Mall, New Street, Malahide, Co Dublin
Tel 8450102
Seating 38
Open 8.30am-5.30pm Mon-Sat; closed Sun
Average £5; £ 2.25 breakfast.
Priscilla's pretty interior and scrubbed pine floors make it ideal for breakfast, morning coffee, lunch or afternoon tea. Specialities are pastries.
Babies/children catered for, child portions. Wheelchair friendly (except toilets). No smoking area (8). Tables outdoors. Ground floor. Stairs to toilets.

Buttercups Coffee Shop
4 Molesworth Place, Dublin 2
Tel 6761040
Seating 30
Open 8am-5pm Mon-Fri
Average £2.55 lunch. Unlicensed
Payment LV
This sandwich bar/coffee shop is conveniently situated for shoppers. Specialities are salads and good breakfasts. Vegetarians are catered for.
Babies/children catered for, child portions. Wheelchair friendly (except toilets). No smoking area (16). Takeaway. Ground floor.

Curry Pot Coffee Shop
45 Prussia Street, Dublin 7
Tel 8681911
Seating 24
Open 8am-8pm Mon-Sat
Average £3 lunch. Unlicensed
The Curry Pot distinguishes itself with reliables like shepherd's pie, Irish stew, and chicken curry. Vegetarian dishes are also available.
Babies/children catered for, child portions and menu. No smoking area (6). Takeaway. Ground floor.

Mimosa Salad Bar
16 Fitzwilliam Lane, Dublin 2
Tel 6616089
Seating 60
Open 7.30am-3pm Mon-Fri; closed Sat/Sun
Average £2.40-3.95 lunch; £2.80 breakfast
Payment TC, LV
A breakfast/lunch restaurant accommodating the vegetarian .

Babies/children allowed. Not wheelchair friendly. No smoking area (25). Takeaway. Ground floor.

Take Five
16a Lincoln Place, Dublin 2
Tel 6609519
Seating 90
Open 7am-8pm Mon-Fri; 7am-5pm Sat; closed Sun.
Average £5; £1.50 minimum 12.15pm-2pm Mon-Fri.
Payment LV
A cafe whose typical fare is serving burger, chips and lasagne. For vegetarians there are salads and vegetable quiche.
Children/babies catered for, 1/2 price child menu. Not wheelchair friendly. No smoking area (25). Takeaway. Ground floor. Stairs.

Gammell's Delicatessen
33 Ranelagh, Dublin 6
Tel 962311
Seating 11
Open 9am-8pm Mon-Sat; 11am-8pm Sun
Average £2.50 main course. Unlicensed
A delicatessen shop specialising in a large selection of salads, wonderful potato cakes at 50p each, as well as wholemeal brown and banana breads. Vegetarians are also catered for.
No smoking area. Takeaway. Ground floor.

Hanky Pancakes
Powerscourt Townhouse, Dublin 2
Tel 6719090
Seating 100
Open 9am-6pm Mon-Sat; 9am-7pm Thurs; closed Sun except mid Nov -Christmas.
Average 95p-£3; unlicensed.
Payment LV.
This established specialist creperie serves both savoury and sweet pancakes Brittany style. Vegetarian available.
Babies/children catered for, child menu. Wheelchair friendly townhouse entrance and toilets. No smoking area (12). Eat-in or takeaway.

Cafe Crepe
15, South Leinster Street, Dublin 2
Tel 6610085
Seating 30
Open 8am-7pm Mon-Sat; closed Sun.
Average £3 lunch. Unlicensed.
Payment , LV, TC,
Crepes for breakfast - served with toast and the morning papers - make a welcome change from continental rolls and coffee although this is also available here. Good espresso is served with the requisite glass of water and pastries are freshly baked on the premises. Vegetarian available.
Babies/children catered for, child menu. Wheelchair friendly (except toilets). No smoking area (13). Takeaway.

Subways
3 South Anne Street, Dublin 2
Tel 6774339
Seating 30
Open 8am-midnight Mon-Thurs

The Owl Restaurant
109A/B Pearse Street, Dublin 2
Tel 6773216
Seating 24
Situated close to the IDA Centre, that showcase of Irish arts and crafts and a must on any tourist itinerary, The Owl specialises in breakfasts. Lunch includes lasagne and quiche and their other speciality is fish and chips at £2.75. Unlike most cafes, this one stays open till 10pm. Ideal for a fish supper.
Babies/children catered for, child portions and menu/ high chairs. No smoking area (10). Takeaway and delivery. Ground floor. Stairs.

The Coffee Inn
7 South Anne Street, Dublin 2
Tel 6719302
Seating 45
Open noon-iam seven days
Average £7.50; £2.50 minimum 12.30pm-2.30pm; house wine £8.50, glass £1.95
Payment LV
Somewhere for a cup of coffee in a slightly downbeat atmosphere. Decor consists of

posters advertising gigs around town. Young and slightly alternatiave at night. You can also sit outside on a sunny day and watch the world go by.
Babies/children catered for, child portions. No smoking are (8). Tables outdoors. Takeaway. Ground floor. Stairs.

Poppies
The Square, Enniskerry, Co Wicklow
Tel 2828869
Seating 40
Open 9am-7pm seven days
Average £6.95; under £3.95 set meals; house wine £7.25.
Payment EC, TC.
Winner of a Tidy Towns Award for Best Shop Front, this homely little shop offers country cooking with specialities like quiches and vegetable dishes.
Babies/children catered for, child portions and menu. Not wheelchair friendly. No smoking area. Private room for parties. Takeaway. Ground floor.

Ron's Restaurant and Guesthouse
50/51 Clontarf Road, Dublin 3
Tel 331595
This self service restaurant, which is also a shop, offers specialities like coddle, steaks and Irish stew, all modestly priced. Roast beef or chicken is £3.50 and the house wine must be one of the cheapest in Dublin. The guesthouse has nine bedrooms, all ensuite.

Belinda's Coffee Shop
15 South Frederick Street, Dublin 2
Tel 6798598
Seating 45
Open 8am-6pm Mon Fri; 10am-4.30pm Sat.
Average £5; £1.75 minimum 12.30pm-2pm; house wine 1/4 bottle £2.15.
Payment LV
This coffee shop prides itself on its flexibility. Proprietor, David O'Keeffe believes the customer is king and sandwiches are of the designer variety. Close to the government buildings, you can TD spot while lunching.
Babies/children catered for, child portions. No smoking area (12). Takeaway. Ground floor.

Johnson's of Dun Laoghaire
21 Upper Georges Street, Dun Laoghaire, Co Dublin
Tel 2804855
Seating 40
Open 8.30 am-6.30pm Mon-Sat; 11am-6pm Sun.
Average £3 main dish; £2.50 breakfast all day. Unlicensed.
Payment LV
Dun Laoghaire's newest coffee shop/sandwich bar is pleasantly decorated with pine surfaces making the interior light and airy. Its 'All Day Breakfast' is particularly popular at the weekend. Lunch dishes go for about £3 and range from lasagne and quiche to savoury pies. There are also homemade apple and rhubarb slices and various types of cakes, all reasonably price.
Babies/children catered for, child portions. No smoking area (8). Takeaway. Ground floor.

Penelope's Cake Shop
14 Orwell Road, Rathgar, Dublin 6
Tel 970204
Seating none
Open 8am-6pm Mon-Sat
Speciality cakes and pastries, made by the owners for the last 32 years, are a favourite with longstanding Rathgar residents as well as their more far-flung customers. Everything - from the five varieties of bread to sausage rolls, tarts and sponges - has an authentic homemade taste and looks freshly baked.
Wheelchair friendly. Takeaway.

Chips with Everything

Fear of frying does not afflict Dubliners - even in these cholesterol fraught days. Areas like O'Connell Street are lined with purveyors of chips with auxiliary supplies coming to the rescue from late-night vans. Connoisseurs put Dublin in the number two spot in the pommes frites stakes, just beind Brussels.

The late-night Italian caffs who were originators of chips in their newspaper twists have now been joined by American chip stylists and both schools have their devotees. The traditional Dublin chip is thick, not too regular in shape and doused with eye-smarting vinegar; health inspectors have banished the printed word but plain no-nonsense newsprint is considered proper livery. Near Christchurch, Burdock's, Dublin's oldest chipper with deep fat fryers until recently powered by a vast coal-stoked range, is considered to be definitive.

The American style chip is more or less defined by McDonald's - thinnish chips of regimental regularity served up in attractive cardboard pouches. Preferred condiment is blood-red ketchup.

For Dubliners, chips exist as a meal on their own, but optional accompaniments are bacon, egg and beans, burgers or fish. Dublinese for fish and chips is a wu' n wu' (one and one).

Cafe Ritz
63 Middle Abbey Street, Dublin 1
Tel 8729210
Seating 160
Open 8am-7pm Mon-Sat
Average £2.50
Payment V; LV.
An institution which has a decided emphasis on chips with everything. You can't miss its red neon sign. A good place for a bite while shopping in the area.
Babies/children catered for, child portions and menu.

Lido Cafe
Sussex Street, Dun Laoghaire, Co Dublin
Tel 2880766
Seating
Open all day Mon-Sat
Average £2 'fry'
Standard cafe fare - chips with everything. Bacon, egg and sausage is a favourite. Cheap. Lots of steam and inexpensive nosh'.

Ritz Cafe
Patrick Street, Dun Laoghaire, Co Dublin
Open: Sun 5pm-midnight, Rest of week 12 noon - 2.30, 5pm- midnight except Tues 12 noon - 2.30pm
Fish and chips cafe, with restaurant upstairs.

Miami Cafe/Restaurant
55 Lower Georges Street, Dun Laoghaire, Co Dublin
Tel. 2806067
Seating 30
Open 11.45am-12.15am Mon-Sat; -1am Sun
Average £2.50
A brightly painted burger joint with a cafe facility. Cheap, cheerful and rather garish. Hamburgers, fry-ups, coffee.

New York, New York
39 Mary Street, Dublin 1
Tel 8724038/873
Seating 200
1 Talbot Street, Dublin 1
Seating 70
Open 10am-6pm Mon-Sat; closed Sun
Average £2.50.
This hamburger restaurant has set its sight on service and hygiene and the customer is the boss. The Irish Quality Association has awarded this small hamburger chain its triple hygiene mark, achieved by only nine other restaurants in Ireland. Only 100% pure beef are used in the burgers here.
Babies/children welcome. No smoking area. Takeaway service.

Mayfair Forte Grill
32 O'Connell Street, Dublin 1
Tel 8747264
Seating 100
Meals served 10am-8.30pm Seven days till 9.30pm Thurs
Average £5.00.
This is a bustling, waitress-service grill with formica topped tables opposite the General Post Office in O'Connell Street. For over 40 years, the Fortes of Dublin have been famous for their enormous selection of ice creams. Of Italian origin, aside from the icecreams, there are Italian dishes on the menu. Spaghetti bolognese at £4.50 or lasagne at £3.50. The clientele is colourful and it is a good place to people watch.
Babies/children catered for. No smoking area.Takeaway service

McDonald's
Chain of hamburger joints. Contact 766444 for details.
With a new flagship restaurant now open in O'Connell street, McDonalds needs no introduction as a fast food eatery. It is clean, efficient and brightly lit with good restroom facilities. Popular with young and old alike, McDonalds offers quick pre-prepared food at affordable prices

Luigi's Fast Food
116 Ranelagh, Ranelagh, Dublin 6
Tel 975089
Seating:35
Open: Mon-Tues 12pm-2am, Rest of week 12pm-4am
Average £1.95
This fast-food restaurant offers good value meals on Monday and Tuesday. The specialities are kebabs and burgers but they do not cater for vegetarians. The interior is rather tatty but where else would you get burger and chips for under £2?
Babies/children catered for, child portions available.

Central Cafe
40/42 Main Street, Blackrock, Co.Dublin
Tel 2990898
Seating 54
Open: Restaurant Mon12pm-2.30pm, Tues-Sat 12pm-10pm, Sun 5pm-10pm, Takeaway Tues-Sat 12pm-1am
Average: £3.50.
Traditional fish and chip shop with predominantly deep pink walls which are hung with framed prints. Table tops are simulated marble and seating consists of upholstered benches. Specialities include burgers and veggie burgers.
Children/babies allowed and catered for on request. Ground floor.

Avalon Grill
63 Georges Street, Dun Laoghaire, Co Dublin
Open noon-2.30pm, 5pm-12.30 midnight Mon-Fri, 5pm-4am Sat, 5pm-12.30 Sun.
Fish, chips and kebabs.

Sounds Diner
60 Bolton Street, Dublin 1
Tel 8720253
Open 11pm-4am Mon-Sat, 11pm-8am Sunday
Average £3.50
Beside the College of Technology in Bolton Street, Sounds' claim to fame is that it opens at 11pm and closes at 4pm, open throughout the night, there for breakfast and still in business for lunch. A clever concept! So if you are peckish in the wee small hours this is for you. Fries are their speciality.
Babies/children allowed. No smoking area. Takeaway.

Fuisciardi's
27 Marlborough Street, Dublin 1
Tel 8741461
Seating 36
Open 11am-6.30pm Mon-Sat, closed Sunday.
Average £3.30 fish, chips and coffee.
A fish and chip shop also serving vegetarian burgers. Some people say they serve the best fresh fish and homemade chips in Dublin. Just as it should be! They also do a four course lunch for £3.25. Unfortunately fish and chips are on the special lunch menu only on Fridays. While not exactly the Ritz, there is a waitress service. As Marlborough Street runs parallel to O'Connell Street, Fusciardi's is close to the shops and several major hotels..
Babies/children catered for. No smoking area. Takeaway.

Byrnes Restaurant
10 Lower Liffey Street, Dublin 1
Tel 8729392
Seating 38
Open 8am-7.30pm Mon-Sat, closed Sunday
Average £1.00-£1.50
A fish and chip restaurant that boasts homemade chips and good value breakfasts
Babies and children catered for and hi-chairs available. good value. Wheelchair friendly except the toilets No smoking area. Takeaway service.

Food Court
5-7 Upper O'Connell Street , Dublin 1
Tel 87244000
Seating:120
Open: 11am-10pm seven days
Average: £3.95
Payment EC, LV
The Food Court offers a variety of fast food and also caters for vegetarians.
Children/babies allowed, hi-chairs, baby changing facilities. Air conditioned. Half restaurant is allocated to no smoking. No private catering. Regular takeaway. Ground floor and lift to toilets.

Hot Plate
32 Upper Liffey Street, Dublin 1
Tel 8730168
Seating 85
Open 8am-6p Mon-Sat, Closed Sunday
Average £3.50 lunch, £2.00 breakfast.
This fast food restaurant close to the major shops and just a skip across the river via the Ha'penny Bridge serves lasagne and breakfast specials as well as vegetarian options. Friendly staff make the visitor feel at home. Bright and cheerful with affordable prices.

Babies and children welcome and catered for. Hi-chairs available and changing facilities. No smoking area. Takeaway.

Kebab House
9/10 Strand Road, Portmarnock, Co Dublin
Tel 8462627
Seating 60
Open noon-3am seven days
Average £2.10, minimum 95p.
This kebab and fast food restaurant caters for the vegetarian along with the kebab enthusiast. A spacious restaurant, serving a mixed but usually quite young clientele. Eat in or takeaway.
Babies/children catered for, half price menu for children. Wheelchair friendly (except toilets). No smoking area.

Jimmy Dean's
73 South Great Georges Street, Dublin 2
Tel 4784864
Seating 47
Open 9am-2am Mon-Thurs, 9am-4am Fri-Sat, 12 noon-3am Sunday
Average £1.55, minimum £2.00 on weekend nights. Breakfast £1.50, lunch £1.50, Kebab £3.00.
A memorial to the late James Dean, who, if he were still alive, would be over 60. It comes complete with original fifties juke box. This fast food diner boasts good burgers and kebabs, while making provision for vegetarians. The quarter pounder burger costs only £1.50. The homemade chips are big, and chilli or garlic sauce will spice them up nicely. Budget eating in the heart of Dublin. In the evening, this is a meeting place for the 18-30 year olds, particularly after the clubs close.
Babies/children catered for. No smoking area. Takeaway.

Mr Burger
17 Westmoreland Street, Dublin 2
4/5 Grafton Street, Dublin 2
8 Upper O'Connell Street, Dublin 1
41 Middle Abbey Street, Dublin 1
Open 10am-4am seven days (exc. Middle Abbey Street 10am-7pm)
Average £1.00 burger and chips
A fast food restaurant with a juke box and a menu featuring a variety of burgers and mixed salads. Winner of a Q Standard Award for their veggie quarter pounder. Money back guarantee if customers are unhappy.
Babies /children welcome and catered for, hi-chairs. Wheelchair friendly (except toilets).No smoking area. Takeaway

Beshoff's
14 Westmoreland Street, Dublin 2
Tel 6778026
Seating 80
Open 11am-11pm Mon-Thurs, Sun. 11am-3am Fri-Sat.
Average £4.00. Set price meal for tourists four courses £4.50.
A fast food fish and chip restaurant minus the plastic utensils of other establishments. The menu provides a variety of deep fried fresh fish with daily specials.
Babies/children welcome, hi-chairs. Wheelchair friendly (except toilets) No smoking area. Takeaway service.

Flash Harry's Diner
18 Main Street, Blackrock, Co Dublin
Tel 2831905
Seating 28
Open 8.30am-2am Mon-Weds; -3am Thurs; -4am Fri/Sat; noon-3am Sun.
Average £2.50 lunch; £2.25 full Irish breakfast
Payment LV.

Leo Burdock's

2 Werburgh Street, Dublin 8
Tel 540306
Open 12.30pm-11pm Mon-Fri; 2pm-11pm Sat; closed Sun/bank holiday.
Average £2.50

Arguably Dublin's best fish and chip shop where the homemade chips are big and thick and the fish is always fresh. Unfortunately, health regulations forbid the wrapping of fish and chips in newspaper.

Pizza 'n' Pasta

As throughout most of the non-Mediterranean world, the pizza boom arrived in Dublin via America rather than Italy. This explains the proliferation of stars and stripe themes and the various Hollywood and Chicago gangster variations.

Filling and affordable are what pizza is all about but when it's freshly baked to order, it doesn't really qualify as fast food - and all the better for that. Lovers of authenticity should be warned that gaelic interpretations can run to pineapple, sweetcorn and even baked beans (yes, really!)

Pizzeria Italia in Temple Bar is an Italian-run exception, offering authentic pizzas with heavily-accented banter and tiny jostling tables that put you in mind of a Neapolitan neighbourhood caff.

The Chicago Pizza Pie Factory is Dublin's largest, part of the UK based chain, and was the first begetter of that carbohydrate depth charge for the seriously hungry - the deep pan pizza. The walls here are lined with pictures of hulking American footballers, no doubt as a warning.

The Bistro Pizza Pasta
4/5 Castle Market, Dublin 2
Tel 6715430
Open 8am-midnight Mon-Thurs; 8am-2am Fri-Sun.
Average £9.50; £2/4 minimum lunch/dinner; house wine £8.75 per litre.
Payment all major credit cards except AmEx; EC, TC, LV
Don't expect starched napkins here. Staff uniforms comprise white t-shirts with Edberg designs and lurid green collars, jeans and sensible shoes. The collars match the walls (except the red brick) and the back wall is a mural of an exaggerated Edwardian eating scene. Nothing exaggerated about the very reclining atmosphere as wood floors and furniture inside contrast with the white plastic upholstery for sun-hoggers outside in a suntrap (Castlemarket) that allows you to eat well for half the price of Cooke's Cafe up the street. A nice touch is the offer of matching your favourite pasta shape with your favourite sauce (e g fusilli carbonara) for £4.95. Two final commendations: leading candidate for best carrot cake (£1.95) and best (though not the largest) cappuccino (90p) in Dublin .
Babies/children catered for, child portions; high chairs. No smoking area (10). Booking advisable weekends. Private room for parties. Pizza takeaway.

Chicago Pizza Pie Factory
St Stephen's Green Centre, St Stephen's Green, Dublin 2
Tel 4787233
Seating 280
Open 11.45am-11.30pm Mon-Sat;12.30pm-11pm Sun
Average £7; lunch from £2.50; house wine £8.25. Fully licensed.
Payment all credit cards except DC; EC, TC, LV. 10% service for eight or more.
Pizza restaurant where staff occasionally dance on the bar and the speciality is deep dish pizza. The holding company runs a chain of American-style pizza restaurants all over Europe. The theme is an American style eatery, but not fast food. The bar is amazing. The posters and pictures on the walls emphasise the Chicago theme. There is a tremendrous buzz on Friday and Saturday evenings. Definitely a place for the young-at-heart. Although dinner tends to be busy, lunch is a more subdued affair but, for a location adjacent to the Stephen's Green Shopping Centre, the price must be one of the best bargains in town. Of special note is the minestrone soup, which is hot and filling and contains a vegetable garden.
Babies/children catered for, child portions and menu. No smoking area (70). Booking advisable. Private room for parties. Takeaway by arrangement. Basement. Stairs.

Pizzaworks
92 Terenure Road North, Dublin 6w

Tel 909036
Seating 60
139 Lower Rathmines Road, Dublin 6
Tel 970078
Seating 14
5 North Street, Swords, Co Dublin
Tel 8408555
Takeaway only
Open 12.30am-12.30pm Mon-Thurs; noon-1am Fri-Sun
Average £7; house wine £7.75.
Payment A, AmEx, V; EC, TC, LV

The Terenure restaurant is like an Amercian fast food diner with pictures of Hollywood stars reinforcing this impression. The 16" pizza is huge and an added bonus is that you can have a bottle of wine with your meal. For 'Americanophiles' - submarine sandwiches are on the menu which also includes burgers, hot dogs, chilli, chicken fingers and chicken burgers.

Babies/children catered for; high chairs. No smoking area (8). Booking advisable. Takeaway plus delivery charge with minimum £4.95.

Pinheads Pizza
14 Rathgar Road, Rathmines, Dublin 6
Tel 972777
Open 5pm-2am Mon-Thurs; 5pm-3am Fri-Sat; 3pm-2am Sun; weekday deliveries 5pm-midnight; weekend up to 1am, 65p; minimum for delivery £4. .
Average £1.80 - £12.10, depending on size and toppings.

Rather nice pizzas for takeaway or delivery. They even half cook the pizza so you can finish it off yourself - especially useful when you have friends around and want the end product to be piping hot! Vegetarian available.

Babies/children allowed. Takeaway. Ground floor.

LaPizza
9/10 Upper Georges Street, Dun Laoghaire, Co Dublin
Tel 2841684
Seating 80
52 Lower O'Connell Street, Dublin1
Tel 8730027
Seating 60
1 St Stephen's Green, Dublin2
Tel 6717175
Seating 100
15 Upper O'Connell Street, Dublin1
Tel 8788010
Seating 80
Open 11am-11pm
Average £10.00; £3.99 for as much as you can eat deep pan ham and mushroom pizza Mon / Tues 5pm-11pm; £2.99 lunch up to 5pm Mon-Fri; house wine £8.65.
Payment all major credit cards; LV

This pizza restaurant is a symphony in green, pleasant, comfortable and excellent value for money. Deep Pan Pizza night is a must for the starving on a strict budget.

Babies/children catered for, child portions and menu. No smoking area (25). Takeaway. Ground floor.

Miller's Pizza Kitchen
9/10 Lower Baggot Street, Dublin 2
Tel 6766098
Seating 75

62 Ranelagh Village, Dublin 6
Tel 975941
Seating 35
52 Upper Baggot Street, Dublin 4
Tel 6606022
Seating 40
Open noon-12.30am Sun-Thurs; till 2.30am Fri/Sat; noon-1am seven days; noon-12.30am Sun-Thurs; till 1am Fri/Sat
Average £7; £3.95 set lunch pizza, coleslaw, tea/coffee; house wine £9.80, glass £1.95.
Payment all major credit cards except DC; EC, TC, LV.

Miller's Pizza Kitchen is situated directly opposite Toner's pub on Baggot Street and is just around the corner from Doheny & Nesbitts and also O'Donoghues. It is the perfect place for an ample pizza or burger either before, during, or after a couple of drinks in any of the above mentioned pubs. It is also very popular on rugby weekends as the crowds leave Lansdowne Road on the move into town in search of food!! Vegetarian available.

Babies/children catered for, child portions; high chairs. No smoking area (10). Booking advisable evenings. Tables outdoors. Takeaway. Ground floor.

Fat Freddies
20 Temple Lane, Dublin 2
Tel 6796769
Seating 82
Open noon-10pm Mon-Thurs; noon-12.30am Fri-Sat, noon-10pm Sun; closed Jan-April, Sept-Oct .
Average £6-7; house wine £9, glass £1.90; corkage £2.
Payment A, V; EC, LV

This pizza restaurant with a predominantly young clientele has entertainment Thurs-Sat consisting of a variety of live music. Bric-a-brac adorns the walls of this most informal of pizza houses. Toilets are an extreme squeeze. Garlic bread is a speciality and their dough is made to order on the premises. Vegetarian calzone (their first in five and a half years) is remarkably tasty. Pizza bases are very thin but doughy and stodgy desserts are a treat but not for slimmers!

Babies/children catered for, child portions; high chairs. Not wheelchair friendly. No smoking area (26). Booking advisable, Private parties up to 40 catered for. Takeaway. Ground floor.

Pizza Stop
6/9 Chatham Lane, Dublin 2
Tel 6796712
Seating 50
Open noon-1am Mon-Sat; 5pm-midnight Sun
Average £9.50; house wine £9.50.
Payment A, V; EC,TC

To find Pizza Stop, walk down Chatham Street, follow your nose and the delicious aromas will take you right there. This must be a trick of the venting systems from the central open plan kitchen! Lunch is reasonably low key but in the evening with a large party, you could find yourself dancing between the tables. The house wine, Chianti de Castellani 1991, is nice and dry but rather light. The Italian bread is made on the premises and the speciality, Lady B - named after a girlfriend of one of the partners - is a chicken dish akin to cacciatore using peppers instead of mushrooms and is served with a generous side salad. Finish off with ice cream, tartufo negro, tartufo bianco or sticky toffee crunch bombe that makes an explosive end to the meal.

Babies/children catered for, child portions and menu. No smoking area (12).Takeaway. Ground floor.

Independent Pizza
8 South Anne Street, Dublin 2
Tel 6795266
Seating 65
46 Lower Drumcondra Road, Dublin 9
Tel 302044
Seating 50
Open 11am-midnight Sun-Thurs; 11am-1am Fri-Sat
Average £5; house wine £7.50, glass £1.65.
Payment all major credit cards except DC; EC, TC, LV

Independent Pizza is, just as the name implies, a pizza restaurant, with a bistro air.

You won't find plastic-topped tables and chairs here. As we go to press it's semi self-service but this will change to waitress service and the managment promise us that the menu is about to expand. There is a limited dessert menu. Pizzas come in various sizes with a choice of 14 toppings. The large will serve two and the medium easily satisfies the hungry. The cheesecake too is nice and creamy. Not a posh eatery but it does a lot better than many with far higher pretensions! A good buzz in a tasty atmosphere. Vegetarian available.
Babies/children catered for, child portions and menu. No smoking area (30). Tables outdoors. Takeaway. Ground floor. Stairs to toilets.

Pappagallo's
Blakes Restaurant, Stillorgan Grove, Stillorgan, Co Dublin.
Tel 2834377
Seating 72
Open 5pm-11.30pm Mon-Thurs; noon-11.30pm Fri-Sun
Average £8.50; £3.95 lunch Fri only; £4 minimum after 6pm; house wine £6.95.
Payment all major credit cards TC, LV.
Pappagallo's is located at the back of the Blake's complex in Stillorgan Grove. The Italianite decor leaves one in no doubt that it is a pizza/pasta restaurant. I had a calzone on my visit, as it is normally a good test of the pizzamaker's art. It took about 20 minutes to appear, an assurance that the food is freshly baked but a deterent for those in a rush. Pizza comes with a mixed side salad. It is meant to add an exotic touch but doesn't. All in all, Pappagallo's provides pizza and pasta in a trattoria type ambience. It offers a good night out without having to take out a mortgage to pay the bill!
Babies/children catered for, child portions and menu; high chairs. No smoking area (40). Tables outdoors. Ground floor. Stairs.

Pizzeria Italia
23 Temple Bar, Dublin 2
Tel 6778528
Seating 18
Open noon-11pm Tues-Sat; closed Mon/Sun
Average £9.50; £5 minimum; house wine £10, glass £2.
Located just off the main thoroughfare of activity in the noisily fashionable Temple Bar area, this cosy little restaurant, with a relaxed chatty atmoshere, is run by Italians. There is no mistaking that connection with the red, white and green of the Italian flag everywhere. The fare ranges from starters of stuffed courgettes or peppers and garlic mushrooms to entrees like Pizza Marguerita, spaghetti vongole and mussels in tomato sauce. Their minestrone soup is definitely homemade and the bread is excellent. Desserts of creme caramel and, not unexpectedly, tiramisu and good cappuccino have all proven a good way to conclude a visit to this pizzeria. The chef clearly knows how it's done, reminding the guest that good pizzerias are not easy to come by.
Babies/children allowed. No smoking area (4). Takeaway. Ground floor.

L & B Pizza Bar
Unit 5a, Shopping Mall, Strand Road, Portmarnock, Co Dublin.
Tel 8462393
Seating 12
Open 9am-midnight seven days
Average £4.50.
Pizza bar, deli and bakery. Vegetarian available. This is the Portmarnock pizzeria, small with convenient opening hours and reasonable prices. L & B also serves as a deli and bakery so you can sit down, eat, then do some shopping. A novel concept.
Babies/children catered for, child portions. No smoking area (12) Tables outdoors. Takeaway and delivery. Ground floor. Stairs.

Bits and Pizzas
15 Patrick Street, Dun Laoghaire, Co Dublin
Tel 2842411
Seating 60
Open noon-midnight seven days.
Average £7; £3.25 lunch special; house wine £8.50.
Payment all major credit cards EC, TC, LV
Up Patrick Street and thus off the main drag is where you'll find Bits and Pizzas. The locals know it and come back. Frank encourages his clientele to submit their comments. Here are some, 'I like my pizza and garlic bread', 'We are tourists from the USA and are very happy with the excellent and courteous service'. The pizzas are enormous and the larger size only for those with huge appetites or perhaps to be shared between two. The speciality - quattro fromaggio - to non-Italian literati means four cheeses, mozzarella, cottage cheese, Parmesan and blue cheese. A bottle of the house wine comes at a very reasonable price. Bits and Pizzas claim to serve the biggest pizzas in town at an affordable price.
Babies/children catered for; high chairs. No smoking area (16). Booking advisable lunch / weekends. Takeaway.

Pizza Express
7 Georges Avenue, Blackrock, Co. Dublin
Tel.2835666
Open 5pm-1am seven days
Average from £2.75; special offers from £3.99
Pizza takeaway. Vegetarian available.

Four Star Pizza
51 Upper Georges Street, Dun Laoghaire, Co Dublin.
Tel.2843629
Open evenings
Various outlets throughout Dublin. Real American pizza delivered to your door.

Bad Ass Bistro
Unit 4, Strand Road, Portmarnock, Co Dublin.
Tel 84461120
Seating 35
Open 1pm-11pm Mon-Sat; 1pm-10pm Sun
Average £10; £3.50 minimum peak hours; house wine £7.95.
Payment all major credit cards EC
A little cafe not to be confused with an establishment of the same name in Temple Bar. This one stands off the main road leading from Portmarnock, looking boldly out to sea. The menu, although principally pizza/pasta, also carries variations of chicken, steaks and burgers. The calamari dreaming starter is sautéd squid in a white wine, tomato and garlic sauce with a squeeze of lemon. The mussels too are very appetising. Verdict - a friendly little seaside cafe with an Italian air. Vegetarian available.
Babies/children catered for, child portions and menu; high chairs. Wheelchair friendly (except toilets). No smoking area (10). Takeaway. Ground floor.

Pizza Place
12 West Pier, Howth, Co Dublin.
Tel 322255
Seating 60
Open 8am-midnight seven days
Average £9; £2.95 breakfast; £4.25 lunch; house wine £8.50.
Payment A, V; EC, TC, LV
Raw brick, pine and rough floors set the interior of Pizza Place. A full breakfast of orange juice, a complete fry including black and white puddings and toast, tea/coffee is

served until noon. When the lunches go on stream, pizzas themselves range from £2.75-£7.75. The seafood variety should be good as the fishing boats dock only feet away from the front door. A wide range of ice-creams are served in interesting ceramic and glass containers. Vegetarian available.
Babies/children catered for, child portions and menu; high chairs. No smoking area (15). Booking advisable weekends. Takeaway.

Rockwells
Talbot House, Killiney Hill, Killiney Road, Co Dublin
Tel 2849888/9
Seating 45
Newly opened pizzeria. Further details unavailable.

The Pizza Cellar
O'Dwyers, 8 Lower Mount Street, Dublin 2
Tel 6761718
Seating 100
Open noon-11pm
Average £10; house wine £8
Pizzeria in a popular pub.
Babies/children catered for, child portions and menu; high chairs and baby changing room.Not wheelchair friendly. No smoking area (30). Takeaway. Ground floor.

South Street Pizza Bar
Unit 4, South Great Georges Street, Dublin 2
Tel 4750421/4752273
Seating 60
Open noon-2am seven days.
Average £12; house wine £9.50.
Payment all major credit cards, LV.
Italian restaurant, popular with students who flock here for their garlic rations, passing the time in basic but bearable surroundings with basic but bearable Chianti. Twenties, thirties style jazz/blues music played over PA system. Specialities are pasta, pizza and chargrilled steaks.
Babies/children catered for. No smoking area (10). Booking advisable. Tables outdoors. Takeaway.

Pizza Connection
The Diamond, Malahide, Co Dublin
Tel 8454223
Seating 50
Cross Gunn's Bridge, Phibsboro, Dublin 7
Tel 307676
Open 5pm-12.30am, 12.30pm-12.30am
Malahide; noon-1am seven days
Average £8; house wine £7.95
The most striking feature about the Malahide branch is the furniture - tables crafted from the eccentric debris of lumberjacks' art with chairs to match. Made by Paul Moore in Portlaoise, they turn the restaurant into a work of art. Expect good food and a house wine reasonably priced. I can recommend the Pizza Neptune - tomato sauce, mozzarella, anchovies, tuna, baby shrimp, oregano and a little garlic on a beautifully crisp base
Babies/children catered for, child portions; high chairs. Not wheelchair friendly. No smoking area (5). Booking advisable. Private room for parties. Takeaway by arrangement. Stairs.

American

American food abroad is just as difficult to define as it is on its home ground. Basically, it's an amalgam of contributions from all the nationalities that make up a great melting pot of a nation.

Hamburgers and frankfurters - alias hot dogs - are Germanic borrowings. Italian pizzas, Mexican tacos, TexMex chilli and Japanese teriyaki have all been annexed and re-energised with stars-and-stripes verve. Dublin's American houses tend to be enthusiastically run by cheerful young staff, attract buzzy crowds and are great value for families. These restaurants were first to treat children like real people and provide high chairs as standard equipment.

Rock Garden
1 Crown Alley, Temple Bar, Dublin 2
Tel 6799114/6799773
Seating 55
Open 12pm-midnight seven days; music venue 8pm - very late.
Average £12; lunch £2.95 Mon-Fri 12pm-2pm; Sunday brunch 12pm-7pm; house wine £8.95.
Payment A; EC, TC, LV. 10% service charge for eight or more.
The Rock Garden is one of the musically hip and trendy places to eat. The original Rock Garden opened in Covent Garden in the mid seventies, the Dublin version just before Christmas 1991.The decor is predominantly black metal, steel, sparse lighting and a long bar with bottles stored appropriately behind steel wires. Tables may be found on the other side on different levels. It is a great place for a drink, or a drink and a meal before heading either downstairs to a gig or on somewhere else. Deep fried mushrooms, potato skins with soured cream (£1.95) and nachos (£2.95) are great starters. The selection of burgers are all served with French fries and vegetarians are catered for. A good value lunch menu attracts a lot of interest not only from the usual clientele but also those in suits. A superb Sunday brunch for about £5 includes a huge portion of chilli dipper - chilli, tacos and guacamole.
Babies/children catered for up to 7pm, child portions; high chairs. No smoking area (8). Booking advisable for large parties. Tables outdoors. Private room for parties. Stairs.

Bad Ass Cafe
9 Crown Alley, Temple Bar, Dublin 2
Tel 6795981
Seating 100
Open 9am -11pm seven days
Average £8.70 tourist menu; minimum charge £3.45 during busy times; house wine glass £1.60.
Payment A. AmEx, V; EC, TC, LV. Service charge not included.
One of the original restaurants in Temple Bar. For years people came to eat here when there was little else happening in the area. Spacious with wooden tables and chairs and old wooden floors, it has the elements of good value - burgers and pizzas served in casual surroundings.. While waiting for your main course, a small salad and a little brown roll appear - perfect for whetting the appetite. The Bad Ass has a popular following among all ages but particularly among the young - it's cheap and good food is served in buzzing surroundings.
Babies/children catered for, child portions and menu; high chairs and baby changing room. No smoking area (9). Booking advisable only for large parties. Takeaway. Ground floor. Stairs to toilets.

Wolfman's Jack's
302 Lower Rathmines Road, Rathmines, Dublin 6
Tel 964836
Seating 120
Open 4pm-12.30pm; brunch Sat 11am
Average £9; house wine £8.75.
Payment all major credit cards except AmEx; EC, TC, LV.
One of the 'original' American fifties' style restaurants that have come into vogue over recent years. The hanging Morris Minor and iced Fiat Bambino over the door add a dash of motoring history à la Hard Rock Cafe but

are a far cry from the Americana on the walls. Specialities are burgers and chicken dishes. Sunday brunch well worth a try - how about eggs benedict for £2.75? Definitely for the young at heart with loud up-beat music!
Babies/children catered for, child portions and menu. No smoking area (35). Takeaway. Ground floor. Stairs to toilets.

Captain America's Restaurant & Bar
1st Floor, 44 Grafton Street, Dublin 2
Tel 6715266
Seating 130
Open 12-10pm Sun-Wed; 12-12.30pm Thur-Sat.
Average £7-8; house wine £6.95; cocktails £2.25 7pm-9pm. Fully licensed.
Payment all major credit cards LV.
The very first American style hamburger restaurant opened in Dublin in 1971. Decor includes a mixture of Colm Henry photographs and American memorabilia. Specialities are hamburgers and Texmex. Vegetarian available.
Babies/children catered for, child portions and menu; high chairs and changing facilities. Not wheelchair friendly. No smoking area (65). Booking advisable. First floor. Stairs to restaurant, toilets.

Sherie's Restaurant
3 Lower Abbey Street, Dublin 1
Tel 8747237
Seating 105
Open 8am-8pm Mon-Sat; closed Sun, Good Friday, Dec 25/26
Average £6.50; £5.50 two course set lunch 12-3pm; house wine £8.95, corkage £3 nominal.
Payment all major credit cards TC, LV.
An American style diner with a wide range, accommodating both vegetarian and carnivore. Their specialities include chicken and fish.
Babies/children catered for, child portions and menu; high chairs and baby changing facilities. No smoking area (12). Takeaway. Ground floor. Stairs to basement.

Frog's City Diner
33 Upper Baggot Street, Dublin 4
Tel 6606568
Seating 70
Open 11am-2am Sun-Thurs; 11am-5amFri/Sat.
Average £7-8; £2.50 minimum all times; wine licence.
Payment LV.
A fast food American diner catering also in salads. Entertainment - loud jukebox.
Babies/children catered for; child portions. No bookings. Takeaway. Ground floor. Stairs down to toilets.

Eddie Rockets City Diner
7 South Anne Street, Dublin 2
Tel 6797340
Main Street, Blackrock, Co Dublin
Tel 2835192
Main Street, Donnybrook, Dublin 4
Tel 2601090
Rathmines, Dublin 6, Tel 973582
Open 11am-1am Sun-Thurs; 11am-4am Fri-Sat
Average £5; £3.50minimum; house wine £8.
Payment TC, LV.

This American house of fun is expanding its tentacles ever wider with a new diner just opened in Donnybrook. The neon green sign emblazoned on the front of the Donnybrook shop simply says 'Eat', which just about sums up the attitude. A very bright interior (very white with fringes of red) right down to the staff attire, gives an appearance of cleanliness. Bar stools are there for solo diners or pairs, (or anyone if it's packed) whilst the tables really can pack a crowd. The chocolate malts are sinful but children (and indeed adults) flock here. The jukebox, the signage and the T-bird imagery all evoke an aspirational early 1960s *Grease*-American epoch.
Babies/children catered for, child portions and menu; high chairs available. No smoking area (7). Tables outdoors. Private parties by arrangement. Takeaway. Ground floor.

Starvin' Marvin's Diner
7 Westmoreland Street, Dublin 2
Tel 6773025
Seating 65
Open 7.30am-1am Sun-Wed; 7am-4am Thurs-Sat.
Average £6.50; house wine £7.95, ⅓ bottle £2.75
Payment A, V; TC, LV
Newly opened on this busy pedestrian thoroughfare, it expands the increasing rash of American diners in the city. Brightly lit, the staff wear turquoise and it houses (allegedly) the only fully-functional visible old jukebox in town. Service on the slow side but may improve with age.
Babies/children catered for, child menu; high chairs and baby changing room in ladies' toilet. Not wheelchair friendly. Tables outdoors. Takeaway by arrangement. Ground floor. Upstairs. Stairs to mezzanine.

Outlaws Rib and Steak House
62 Upper George's Street, Dun Laoghaire, Co Dublin
Tel 2842817
Seating 30
Open 5.30pm-11pm Sun-Thurs; 11.30pm Fri/Sat
Average £12; £3.95 minimum busy times; house wine £7.50.
Payment all major credit cards except AmEx; EC, TC. 10% service charge.
In existence for over four years, this informal American restaurant is about the size of your mother's old kitchen - before the new extension! Old board barrels and bar give the feel of a wild west saloon, the menu is unmistakeably American. Specialities are burgers, steaks, chicken wings and ribs.
Babies/children catered for, child portions and menu; high chairs available. No smoking area (2). Booking advisable. Ground floor.

SOUTH ANNE ST., D2. • MAIN ST., BLACKROCK • MAIN ST., RATHMINES

French

Many a foodie dates his gastronomic birth from the date of his first meal in France. Whether the first experience was in a truckies' routier or a glittering multi-starred restaurant, it was evident that food was to be taken very seriously indeed. Somebody said once that wondering if a French person was interested in food was like wondering if an alcoholic took a drink.

It was actually the French who invented restaurants and names like Carome and Escoffier set the goalposts for chefs all over the world to emulate. Then a group of French chefs in the seventies exploded the bombshell of nouvelle cuisine and things would never again be the same.

Patrick Guilbaud's restaurant was not only the city's first purpose-built restaurant but under its super-smart roof, Dubliners met their first breathtakingly arranged morsels of nouvelle style. A decade and more on, things have modified, not only in Guilbaud's but in the myriad restaurants that took up the fashion cuisine. Never again will serious restaurants serve up mountains of food in floury, stodgy sauces.

The French buzz now is back to regional cookery and *cuisine granmere* in the restaurants. By their cassoulet, confit of duck and lentils shall you know them.

L'Auberge
41-43 Shelbourne Road, Ballsbridge, Dublin 4
Tel 6608087
Seating 40
Open 12.30pm- 2.30pm Mon-Fri; 6.45pm-10.30pm Mon-Sat
Average £17; £15 table d'hote dinner; £7 lunch; house wine £9
Payment all major credit cards; EC, TC. 12 ½% service.
Previously known as the Osprey, this is a lovely little French restaurant. A big open fireplace and pebbled glass window give the impression of a cottage interior. This setting is presided over by John; his wit and charm are all part of the atmosphere, so is the taped music - best described as camp. A venue that seems much favoured by Amercicans, but then the Embassy is nearby as are the tourist hotels. Don't expect express service, but being patient certainly pays off. Ask regulars who come back week after week.
Babies/children allowed but not catered for. No smoking area (20). Booking advisable. Private room for parties. Ground floor. Stairs to toilets.

Number 10
Lower Fitzwilliam Street, Dublin 2
Tel 6761367
Seating 30
Open 12.30pm-2.30pm Mon-Fri; 6.30pm-10.00pm Mon-Thurs; 6.30pm-11pm Fri; 7pm-11pm Sat; 7pm-9pm Sun
Average £12-13 lunch; £17 or £21 lunch à la carte; house wine £9.95
Payment all major credit cards; EC, TC.
The basement under this elegant 18th century townhouse off Merrion Square has been turned into a charming restaurant, primarily to service the hotel above, but nevertheless attracting a large outside clientele. Rural murals and lots of light colours dispel any gloom typical of some basement dining rooms. The chef is exceptionally competent and the menu is a fairly classical version of modern French cuisine. One speciality which can be recommended is confit of duck. With friendly and efficient service, it is an attractive venue suitable for either a romantic evening or a business lunch. Vegetarian available.
Wheelchair friendly (lift from ground floor). Booking advisable. Private drawing room for 16-20. Basement. Stairs.

Restaurant Patrick Guilbaud
46 James Place, off Lower Baggot St, Dublin 2
Tel 6764192
Seating 75
Open 12.30pm-2pm, 7.30pm-10.15pm Tues-Sat
Average £15.50 set lunch; £25 set dinner; house wine £13-19.

Payment all major credit cards, EC, TC.
15% service.
Unique here in the late seventies, this elegant French restaurant was one of the first to make dining fashionable among Dublin's beau monde. Decor is modern and sophisticated with a great glass dome and hanging greenery. The speciality of the night I ate there was roast duck from Challans with a Seville orange and ginger sauce. Here food is an art form and some of the finest meals in the country are produced. Service is swift, discreet and very French, which attracts its clientele of businessmen, their dark suits relieved occasionally by bright colours worn by women diners. The only Michelin star restaurant in Dublin and the one with most other awards
Babies/children allowed; high chairs available. No smoking area. Booking advisable. Private room for parties. Takeaway by arrangement. Smart dress. Ground floor. Stairs to toilets.

Les Freres Jacques
94 Dame Street, Dublin 2
Tel 6794555
Seating 65
Open 12.30pm-2.30pm Mon-Fri; 7.30pm-10.30pm Mon-Sat; 7.30-11pm Fri-Sat; closed Sun
Average £13 lunch; £20 table d'hote; a la carte £25-28; house wine £10.50.
Payment all major credit cards except DC; EC, TC. 12 ½% service.
Beside the Olympia Theatre in the heart of old Dublin, the atmosphere is instantly French. Food is modern - post nouvelle cuisine - and usually very good. Having started off in Cork, Jean Jacques Caillabet has been in Ireland for many years and having experimented with ways of bringing French food to the Irish diner, at Les Frères Jacques he seems to have found a successful solution. This is due in no small way to his daily forays to the fish or fruit and vegetable market just across the Liffey. Here he can have his pick of fresh produce which in turn his French staff serve with Gallic aplomb. Egon Ronay, Michelin and Good Food Guide. Entertainment - live piano music three nights 8pm-midnight - gives a bistro like air. Specialities are fish and seafood. Vegetarian on request.
Babies/children catered for, child portions. Not really wheelchair friendly. No smoking area (20). Booking advisable. Private room for parties of 12-40. Ground floor. Stairs

Coffers Restaurant
6 Cope Street, Temple Bar, Dublin 2
Tel 6715740/6715900
Seating 45
Open 12.30-2.30pm Mon-Fri; 6pm-11pm Mon-Sat; closed Sun
Average £15; £11 four course pre-theatre; £15.50 four course table d'hote; house wine £9.95.
Fully licensed.
Payment all major credit cards; TC, LV.
10% service.
On the fringe of Temple Bar, Dublin's cosmopolitan left bank, with the Olympia just up the road, this unpretentious restaurant is popular for pre theatre suppers. For many years a steak house, although steak still features prominently, the menu has broadened to include French and continental dishes. Specialities are steak and fish in season. Vegetarian by request.
Babies/children allowed. No smoking area (23). Booking advisable, Private room for parties up to 35. Neat casual dress. Ground floor only. Stairs to toilets.

Pigalle Restaurant
14 Temple Bar, Dublin 2
Tel 6719262/6796602
Seating 60
Open 12.30pm-3pm Mon-Fri; 6.30pm-11pm Mon-Sat.
Average £18.50 six courses; £11.50 lunch; house wine £10.
Payment all major credit cards except AmEx; EC, TC. 10% service.
French restaurant in Temple Bar, more in common with "Le Quartier Latin" than La Place Pigalle. Still, this cosy upstairs restaurant has lots of warm wood and white walls, while window ledges abound with

exotic tropical plants. Linen tablecloths and attractively arranged napkins complete the picture. Strictly table d'hôte, the menu depends upon the season and availability of market produce. During the week individual dishes priced separately can be ordered. However, at weekends the full six course meal is de rigueur! This is an overlooked restaurant which ranks with the best in town. Vegetarian on request.
Babies/children catered for, child portions and menu; high chairs and baby changing room. Not wheelchair friendly. No smoking area (10). Booking essential at weekends. Stairs.

L'Ecrivain
112 Lower Baggot Street, Dublin 2
Tel 6611919
Seating 36
Open 12.30pm-2.30pm Mon-Fri; 6.30pm-11pm Mon-Sat.
Average £25.00; £13.50 lunch; £20.95 table d'hote dinner; house wine £9.75.
Payment all major credit cards; EC, TC.
10% service.
A small French restaurant tucked away in a basement at the corner of Baggot and Fitzwilliam Streets, L'Ecrivain is located under the Fitzwilliam, a private hotel. While the decor is not over-elaborate, chef-proprietor Derry Clarke has a string of accolades which would suggest this is a very special place. These include Eurotocque Bronze Medal Chefs of Ireland and RAI awards. The varied menu changes with the season. Dinner features delicacies like baked rock oysters, mille feuille de saumon and roasted baby chicken. The set-price lunch offers west coast mussels and includes a vegetarian dish of the day. The homemade breads are extraordinary. Worth a visit if your budget stretches to it but, for a restaurant of this calibre, the desserts are a disappointment. Specialities are lamb and game. Vegetarian available; any dietary requirements by arrangement.
Children over eight catered for, child portions and menu to order. Not wheelchair friendly. No smoking area (12). Booking advisable. Takeaway by arrangement. Casual elegant dress. Stairs.

La Grenouille
64 South William Street, Dublin 2
Tel 6779157
Seating 36
Open noon-2.30pm Mon-Sat; 5.30pm-11.30pm Sun-Thurs; 5.30pm-midnight Fri/Sat.
Average £17; £7.50 set price lunch; £16.95 table d'hote dinner; £9.50 early bird;
house wine £9.50.
Payment all major credit cards; EC.
12 ½% service.
French restaurant under new management with a cave-like atmosphere and cobbled floor. Chef Mark, previously second chef at Kilkea Castle, went on to open his own restaurant in Corfu. With a mixture of French and European cooking, he prides himself on his monkfish with red peppers, and for those whose taste runs to turf rather then surf, he recommends fillet of beef with wild mushrooms. A pleasant little cellar restaurant with friendly service. Speciality: supreme of salmon with rhubarb sauce. Vegetarian available.
Babies/children catered for, child portions. Not wheelchair friendly. No smoking area (8). Booking advisable. Private room for parties. Ground floor.

Le Mistral
16 Harcourt Street, Dublin 2
Tel 4781662
Seating 60
Open 12.30pm-2.30pm, 7pm-11pm Mon-Thurs; -11.30pm Fri/Sat; no lunch Sat; closed Sun
Average £18.95 four courses, no coffee; £12.95 lunch three courses, no coffee; house wine £9.50.
Payment all major credit cards except DC; EC, TC. 12 ½% service.
French provençale restaurant where a fresh fish tray is displayed daily. Opened early this year, chef proprietor Philippe Misischi (ex Les Frères Jacques) has created a French ambience from his French staff right down to the wine cellar (which contains a selection

of 60 French wines) and copper pans overhanging the black varnished stove. Entertainment: Wharfdale - assisted piped Parisian music; live piano Thurs-Sat. Speciality is fish, purchased every four days at Smithfield. Vegetarian available.
Babies/children catered for, child portions. Not really wheelchair friendly. No smoking area (30). Booking advisable. Private room for parties Mon-Wed. Tables outdoors on terrace. Smart neat dress. Ground floor. Basement toilets.

Le Coq Hardi
35 Pembroke Road, Dublin 4
Tel 6689070
Seating 50
Open 12.30pm-2.30pm Mon-Fri; 7pm-11pm Mon-Sat; closed Sun and bank holidays
Average £25.00; £14.75 four course set lunch; £24 four course set dinner; house wine £16.00. Fully licensed.
Payment all major credit cards; EC, TC.
12 ½% service.
Less than 15 years ago, John Howard was criticised by a food critic for the lack on his wine list. Today the proprietor of Le Coq Hardi, perched in a Georgian house on a corner of Pembroke Road, has assembled one of the finest connoisseurs' lists in the British Isles, comprising some 700 wines. The finery of the decor is matched by the overwrought professionalism of service and the immaculate French-touched country cuisine, with all the pomp of a men's club. Sometime this year avail of lunch at £14.75.
Not suitable for babies/children. Not wheelchair friendly. No smoking area. Booking advisable. Private room for parties up to 35. Neat dress. Ground floor.

Indian

The old Dublin quip was that most Irishmen had never tasted a curry sober. That was because until recently, curry was the province of the late-night Chinese restaurants, only refuge after pub closing time.

The golden age of authentic Indian food was pioneered by Jimmy's New Delhi in Camden Street and Mike Butt's Golden Orient in Leeson Street. This last was later to spawn The Tandoori Rooms downstairs, Dublin's first posh Indian restaurant, complete with dance floor, designer smart interior and authentic regional food. Now only a happy memory, The Tandoori Rooms' natural inheritor is the fashionable Rajdoot Tandoori which specialises in the sophisticated cuisine of the Northern moghuls, attracting an amazing number of visiting pop stars and celebrities.

Options for Indian food at all levels have increased enormously in the past ten years, not unrelated it seems, to the popularity of ethnic cookery at home and the proliferation of Indian food products backed by advertising and information campaigns. Rogan josh and tikka masala hold no terrors for a population accustomed to seeing the names alongside the cabbages and cornflakes in the supermarket.

Lal Qila "The Red Fort"
27 Lower Georges Street, Dun Laoghaire, Co Dublin
Tel.2804376/2844984 for delivery
Open 5pm-midnight Sun/Mon; 5.30pm-12.30am Tues-Thurs; 5.30-1am Fri/Sat; Mon-Fri noon-2.30am Mon-Fri.
Average £5.50 curry and rice.
Payment A, V; TC. 50p delivery charge within three mile radius; outside radius by special arrangement.
Indian/tandoori full restaurant menu - 'We bring the restaurant to you'. Good value lunch menu, vegetarian recommended.
Children welcome. Catering for functions. Strictly takeaway.

Krishna Indian Restaurant
1st Floor, 47 Lower George's Street, Dun Laoghaire, Co Dublin
Tel 2801855
Seating 32
Open 12.30pm-2.30pm Tues-Sun; 6pm-midnight Sun-Thurs; 6pm-1am Fri/Sat
Average £15; house wine £8.50, glass £1.85.
Payment all major credit cards; EC, LV
10% service. Discount vouchers from time to time.
Indian restaurant specialising in Punjabi food and using free-range chickens and organic vegetables . Small intimate family-run restaurant decorated with Indian wall-hangings. Hanging lamps make this a cosy venue for a romantic evening. Main courses include chicken tikka masala and beef gholan dhost. Their selection of breads are a delicious alternative to rice. Specialities are organic lamb and beef. Vegetarian available.
Babies/children catered for, child portions. Not wheelchair friendly. Takeaway, delivery within three mile radius

Al-Minar Tandoori Restaurant
21 Castle Street, Dalkey, Co Dublin
Tel 2850552/2840900
Seating 64
Open noon- 2.30pm, 6pm-11.30pm seven days.
Average £15.50 four courses, £6.50 minimum; house wine £8.
Payment all major credit cards; EC, TC.
12% service.
Richly authentic, this restaurant is more comfortable - and large enough for big parties - than most, the atmosphere has just the right blend of candlelight, ornaments and delicious aromas. Although relatively expensive, the extra expense is well justified. The traditional tandoori must be one of the best takeaways in Dublin. Vegetarian available.
Babies/children allowed. No smoking area (14). Booking advisable. Private parties catered for. Takeaway.

Sitar Indian Restaurant
18 Merrion Row, Dublin 2
Tel 6615095
Seating 39
Open 6pm-1am seven days
Average £13.50; house wine £8.50.
Payment all major credit cards except DC; EC, TC. 10% service.
Indian restaurant. Speciality vegetarian dishes.
Babies/children allowed. No smoking area (12). Booking advisable weekends. Takeaway. Ground floor.

Jewel In The Crown
5 South William Street, Dublin 2
Tel 6799106
Seating 34
Open 6pm-1am Sun-Thurs; 6pm-2am Fri/Sat
Average £10; £7.95 minimum; house wine £8.95.
Payment all major credit cards except DC; TC.
Newly-opened tandoori restaurant in the heart of Dublin brings the full range of traditional food from the Mughal Shahi kitchen. Vegetarian available.
Babies/children allowed. Wheelchair friendly (except toilets). No smoking area (8). Booking advisable. Takeaway. Ground floor. Stairs down to toilets.

Rajdoot Tandoori
26/28 Clarendon Street, Westbury Centre, Dublin 2
Tel 6794274
Seating 96
Open noon-2.30pm, 6.30pm-11.30pm Mon-Sat; closed Sun
Average £16; £6.95 set lunch; £14.50 dinner; house wine £8.85.
Payment all major credit cards; EC, TC. 12 ½% service on lunch.
An exotic setting sets the scene for this North Indian restaurant which opened here in 1984 in the heart of fashionable Dublin, the first of its kind in Dublin. Winner of Walker's Best Ethnic Vegetarian Restaurant Award 1988. The executive lunch is excellent value in this sumptuous setting. Main courses include prawn bhuna accompanied with pilau rice and lentils; moghlai tandoori and chicken tikka. The food presentation is excellent and the hot towel proffered after the main course is a civilised touch that other establishments would do well to take up. Good value for money. Speciality is tandoori. Vegetarian available
Babies/children catered for; high chairs. Wheelchair friendly (except toilets). No smoking area (14). Takeaway. Casual neat dress. Ground floor. Stairs.

Raj Dhani Tandoori Restaurant
5 South Richmond Street, Dublin 2
Tel 4751808/4751778
Seating 48
Open noon-2pm, 6pm-1,30am
Average £9.50; £5.55 set lunch; house wine £10.20.
Payment all major credit cards except AmEx; EC, TC. 12% service at lunch
The Raj Dhani stays open late and is a great favourite after closing time. Vegetarian available.
Babies/children catered for, child portions. No smoking area (16). Booking advisable. Takeaway/ delivery. Ground floor. Stairs to toilets.

Eastern Raga Indian Restaurant
7 Georges Ave, Blackrock, Co Dublin
Tel 2880220
Open 5pm-1am Mon-Sun
South Indian restaurant.
Takeaway

Chandni Restaurant
174 Pembroke Road, Ballsbridge, Dublin 4
Tel 6681458
Seating 84
Open 12.30pm-2.30pm Mon-Fri; 6pm-10.30pm Mon-Thurs; 6pm-midnight Fri-Sun
Average £15; £7.50 minimum at dinner only; £7.95 set lunch; £12.95 vegetarian; house wine £8.50, glass £1.95.
Payment all major credit cards; EC, TC. 12 ½% service.
Elegant Indian restaurant offers gallery dining overlooking a central atrium. Entertainment live music and dancers nightly. Northern Indian cusine. The selection of desserts is interesting,

try nabdi from Kashuim made from milk and cream with an almond aftertaste. Speciality is chooza masala. Vegetarian available
No smoking area (6). Booking essential weekends. Air conditioned. Private room for parties. Takeaway by arrangement. Smart, casual dress. Ground floor. Stairs.

Royal Tandoori
51 South King Street, Dublin 2
Tel 6778408
Seating 60
Open noon-12.30pm, 6pm-11.30pm Mon-Thurs; 6pm-12.30am Fri/Sat; closed Sun.
Average £15; £6.95 four course lunch, menu changes daily; £7.95 minimum evening; £39.95 set dinner for two; house wine £9.
Payment all major credit cards; EC.
12 ½% service.
Indian restaurant. Chef is from New Delhi. Manager Nazhiel managed Bombay Taj Mahal. Speciality is Royal Tandoori mix - mix of kebabs. Vegetarian available.
Babies/children catered for, child portions. No smoking area (16). Booking advisable. Takeaway/ delivery planned.

Taj Mahal Indian Restaurant
17 Lincoln Place, Dublin 2
Tel 6760568
Seating 62
Open 6pm-1am seven days.
Average £12; house wine £9.95.
Payment all major credit cards; EC, TC.
10% service.
Tandoori restaurant and Dublin's oldest Indian restaurant where draped lamps and multi-coloured artificial flowers set the tone. Recommended is thaki, an assortment of curries and rice served with naan bread. Comprehensive wine list. Speciality tandoori mixed grill, chicken tikka masala. Vegetarian available.
Babies/children catered for, child portions. No smoking area (10). Booking advisable. Private room for parties. Takeaway by arrangement. Ground floor. Stairs to toilets.

Eastern Tandoori
34-35 South William Street, Dublin 2
Tel 6710428
Old Parish Hall, Kill Lane, Deansgrange, Co Dublin
Tel 2892856
1 New Street, Malahide, Co Dublin
Tel 8454154
Seating 64; 68; 48
Open noon 2.30pm Mon-Sat, 6pm-11.30pm seven days (Dublin); noon-2.30 seven days (Deansgrange); 6pm-11.30pm (Malahide)
Average £16; £9.50 minimum dinner; £7.50 set lunch; house wine £11.50. Fully licensed.
Payment all major credit cards, EC, TC.
12 ½% service.
Only Indian restaurant in the Good Food Guide 1990 and Michelin Guide. Legend has it that long ago there lived a famous Moghul King whose life's ambition was to enjoy only the finest food. To this end, the 20 royal chefs were sent out to discover the missing delights. The Eastern Tandoori is like that king's dining room with elaborate-carved high-backed chairs and velvet inlaid wall panels. Tandoori mackerel starter is interesting but beware the bones. Hot towels between courses are a civilised touch. Another good touch is that the customer can decide on the spiciness of the meal. Speciality is tandoori. Vegetarian available.
Babies/children allowed. Not wheelchair friendly. No smoking area (20). Booking advisable. Takeaway. Ground floor. Stairs.

Shalimar Restaurant
17 South Great Georges Street, Dublin 2
Tel 6710738
Seating 56
Open noon-2.30pm Mon-Sat; 6-midnight Sun-Thurs; 6pm-12.30am Fri/Sat
Average £15; £6.95 set lunch; vegetarian table d'hote £14.95; £15.95 fish; £16.95 meat; £6.95 minimum evening; house wine £9.75
Payment all major credit cards; EC, TC.
10% service.
This restaurant, which takes its name from the gardens of the Shah Jahan who built the Taj Mahal in Lahore as a monument of love to his

wife, is centrally situated and is quite smart in a decidedly western sense. The menu, based on northern Indian cuisine which specialises in tandoori dishes, is vast. Also available are breads, naan and fried paratha. Vegetarian available.

Babies/chilldren catered for, child portions; high chairs. No smoking area (9). Booking advisable. Neat, casual dress. Takeaway. Ground floor. Stairs.

Negi Restaurant

Orwell Lodge Hotel
77 Orwell Road, Rathgar, Dublin 6
Tel 977258
Seating 60
Open 12.30pm-2.30pm; 6.30pm-10.30pm; till 9pm Sun
Average £14-15; £16.95 five course set price; house wine £9. Fully licensed.
Payment all major credit cards; EC, TC, LV. 12½% service

This family-run hotel on Dublin's residential south side is about three miles from the city centre. The restaurant takes its name from the owner/chef who purchased the hotel five years ago. Mr Negi, who is Indian, runs the business with his Irish wife, and the restaurant has become very popular for its Indian cuisine. Specialities are tikka, prawns and spiced lamb cutlets. Vegetarian available.

Babies/children catered for, child portions and menu; high chairs and baby changing room. Not wheelchair friendly. No smoking area (30). Booking advisable weekends. Private parties catered for. Ground floor.

Irish

Foreign visitors and corporate entertainers are most likely to be seekers of Irish speciality houses, although certain classics like Irish stew, smoked salmon and brown bread are almost universally available.
Most diners will know about corned beef and cabbage, soda bread and crubeens, but may be a bit flummoxed to see Dublin Bay lawyer on the menu, as it is in Harrisons. It is not one of the denizens of the Four Cold Mines (as the Four Courts have been dubbed), but a gloriously buttered and brandied lobster. Could it be the grasping claws that inspired the name?

Out-of-towners would be well advised not to bring natives with them to Irish speciality houses, as no Irishman is ever happy with a dish that isn't exactly as his mother/granny made it.

Harrisons
29 Westmoreland Street, Dublin 2
Tel 6799373/6799664
Seating 60
Open noon-10.30pm seven days
Average £10; £7.50 up to 6.30pm early bird four courses; £12.50 house menu; house wine £8.50. Fully licensed.
Payment all major credit cards; EC, TC, LV
This restaurant occupies the premises of what was Harrison and Company Confectioners, dating back to 1896. Harrisons has a long and rich literary association including references in James Joyce's *Ulysses*. Piano and live blues/ jazz / traditional music entertainment. Chef Terry Flannagan is on a panel of chefs for Ireland and one of the restaurant's recipes "Chicken Irish Mist" appears in *Gourmet International*. Other dishes include roasted chicken with three old grapes (£6.75), roeheavy lax - or wild Irish salmon to the uninitiated (£9.50) and, subject to availability, Dublin Bay lawyer (£12.95). The speciality is Joycean cuisine. Vegetarian available.
Babies/children catered for, child portions and unofficial menu; high chairs and baby changing room. Braille menu available. No smoking area (20). Booking advisable. Tables outdoors especially on Bloomsday. Private parties catered for up to 60. Basement toilets.

Gallagher's Boxty House
20/21 Temple Bar, Dublin 2
Tel 6772762
Seating 70
Open 12.30pm-11.30pm seven days
Average £10; house wine £7.95. Fully licensed.
A traditional Irish restaurant which, like Irish cuisine, provides stable fare. Run like an old Irish boarding house, an extremely homey and hospitable atmosphere is complemented by two open fires and the continuous din of Irish music. The fare is good and reasonably priced with boxty - an Irish potato pancake - the speciality. Portions tend to fall short of typical Irish meals but are nevertheless good value. This is very much a tourist-aimed establishment, substantiated by the appearance outside of the menu in four languages. Vegetarian available.
Babies/children catered for; improvised child portions; high chairs No smoking area (18). Tables outdoors. Private room downstairs for parties. Takeaway by arrangement. Ground floor and downstairs. Stairs.

Oliver St John Gogarty
58/59 Fleet Street, Dublin 2
Tel 6711822
Seating 70
Open 5pm-11.30pm seven nights; noon-11pm bar food.
Average £13; house wine £9.95. Fully licensed.
Payment all major credit cards; EC, TC, LV.
Cocktails served. Traditional music every night. Traditional Irish restaurant. Speciality fish. Vegetarian available.
Babies/children catered for, ½ portions. Not wheelchair friendly. Private room for parties. Ground floor. Lift.

Oisíns Irish Restaurant
31 Upper Camden Street, Dublin 2
Tel 4753433
Open 7pm-10.30pm seven nights.
Average £35; £27 set county menu; £27 set city menu; house wine £11.50.
Payment all major credit cards; EC, TC.
15% service

Somewhere really different, a genuine Irish restaurant serving traditional Irish dishes with a French touch: like nettle and spinach soup with lots of cream. Dublin coddle, in which gammon is used instead of bacon to give a sharp rather than a salty flavour, and dulse is used in sauces, especially with salmon. The real taste of the sea. Naturally, they also boast Irish stew, not like mother used to make - she never spent two days boiling the bones! If you think Irish food is meat and two overcooked veg, you're in for a surprise. The meal started with tiny sausages flambed in poteen. My companion had garlic mussels in a cider broth. My coddle - the traditional Dublin dish - came with a quail's egg. We followed this exotic domestic adventure with spiced beef, cooked in Guinness and I had the Irish stew. Dessert was bread and butter pudding which tasted more like a cake. Presentation was superb and, although not cheap, Oisins provides an adventure in eating the like of which, unfortunately, is rare in Dublin.

Babies/children catered for, child portions. Not wheelchair friendly. No smoking area available. Booking advisable. Takeaway by arrangement. Stairs.

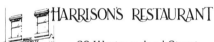

Italian

Italian restaurants have benefitted from the current trendiness of all things Mediterranean and the health gurus' embracing of olive oil, pasta and lush salads.

Unfortunately, menus haven't moved on much from the cannelloni, lasagne and veal dishes they offered 20 years ago.

Best bet for innovative Italian food is in some of the younger, casual places where fresh pasta is made daily and fresh herbs, pesto and carbonara offer respite from the tired bolognese of yesteryear.

Vegetarians can often be happily accommodated by Italian restaurants with tasty choices to tempt even dedicated carnivores - melanzane parmigiana; aubergine cooked with tomatoes and a melting cheese topping; pasta with basil; pine kernels and Parmesan sauce and creamy vegetable lasagne.

The scope here for lively Italian restaurants offering some of the superb regional cuisine has never been realised and the chances of finding some of the exquisite Italian ice creams are very slim indeed.

Pasta Fresca

3-4 Chatham Street, Dublin 2
Tel 6792402/6798965
Seating 75
Open 8am-11.30pm Mon-Sat; closed Sun except Dec/Jan
Average £7 lunch; £11 dinner; £5 minimum 12.30pm-2pm; £5 set meal pasta and drink; £8.50 theatre supper including ½ carafe wine; Italian house wine £9.75
Payment A, V; EC.

Decent Italian food: prepared quickly in jam-packed modernist cafe surroundings, with black ceramic tiled floor and white walls decorated with large prints and posters. On entry, a chilled cabinet displays every conceivable pasta shape and all the sauces from which your meal can be selected. There is also a range of Italian delicatessen products - olive oil, pine kernels, all sorts of cheeses, espresso coffee. Proprietor May Frisby has attracted quite a circle of beautiful people who sip languidly at their cappuccinos. The food is good and the restaurant has established a reputation as a place to eat and meet well and informally. Speciality is fresh homemade pasta. Vegetarian available.

Babies/children catered for, child portions during the day. No smoking area (20). Booking advisable. Private parties catered for. Tables outdoors. Takeaway pasta, sauces, deli. Ground floor.

Ristorante Bucci

7 Lower Camden Street, Dublin 2
Tel 4751000
Seating 50-60
Open noon-3pm Mon-Fri; noon-midnight Fri/Sat; 5.30-10-30 Sun-Thurs
Average £10; £3.95 lunch; £4.95 evening. House wine £7.95. glass £1.75
Payment all major credit cards except AmEx; TC, TC, LV. 10% service for six or more.

Ristorante Bucci is quietly establishing itself a major reputation among the cognoscenti at Dublin's high tables and a real attempt is being made to blend an extremely high standard of food quality with what is fast becoming Dublin's longest list of Italian wines. The proprietor, incidentally, has deliberately sought out smaller quality vineyards and has on hand a selection of three or four Verdicchios, Soaves and Orvietos, as well as a fine representation of Chardonnays and Pinot Grigio. Very serious indeed. Foodwise, zucchini dorati comes recommended as a starter, as well as the parmigiana baked aubergine with carrietiera sauce, mozzarella and parmesan. Pasta features largely among main courses - cannelloni Bucci with its unusual filling of crabmeat and spinach is particularly good but there is also a selection of chicken, pizza and steaks. The kitchen is open-plan so diners can see their meal being prepared; some customers have been known to go and make their own pizza!

Babies/children catered for, child portions. Not wheelchair friendly. No smoking area (10). Booking advisable. Takeaway by arrangement. Ground floor.

Coras Restaurant
1 St Mary's Road, Ballsbridge, Dublin 4
Tel 6600585
Seating 50
Open 8.30am-6pm Mon-Fri; 9.30am-3pm Sun
Average £6.90; £2.50 minimum 12.30pm-2pm; £9.70 four course Sunday lunch; house wine £8
Payment TC.
Italian restaurant whose speciality is pasta. Cora's is a treasure tucked away off Upper Baggot Street, little known to tourists, but well patronised by regulars and a strong following from the Italian community - particularly for their Sunday family lunch when there is always a fleet of Alfa Romeos and Fiats outside. Unlike me - who ordered steak and kidney pie - (not homemade, but good value at £2.50) have the pasta or pizza or a simple chicken dish. Desserts include homemade cheesecake with a delicious crunchy biscuit base and a superb tiramisu. The cappuccino and espresso are unsurpassed. Don't be put off by its utilitarian 1960s formica, Cora's is an institution. Vegetarian available. *Babies/children catered for, child portions. No smoking area (25). Booking advisable especially on Sunday. Tables outdoors. Takeaway by arrangement. Ground floor.*

La Mezza Luna
1 Temple Lane, Dublin 2
Tel 6712840
Seating 70
Open 12.30pm-11pm Mon-thurs; 12.30pm-11.30pm Fri/Sat; 5pm-10.30pm Sun
Average £11; house wine £9.25
Payment A. 10% service for eight or more.
Very popular city-centre Italian restaurant with highly laid-back atmosphere. Staff are not just indigenous Irish, but international so that, as a result, service can be varied and even amusing. A popular stop-off point for celebrities wishing to eschew more obvious haunts, the benched tables are ideal for groups who want to really undo their collective social straitjacket. While the menu is not strictly Italian, for kick-off, the hummus is particularly good. Main courses are fairly priced and usually of a high standard but the desserts are choice - especially the chocolate mousse,

when available.
Babies/children catered for, child portions. Not wheelchair friendly. No smoking area (12). Booking advisable. Takeaway. Ground floor. Stairs.

Napoli Restaurant
2-3 Cumberland Street, Dun Laoghaire, Co Dublin
Tel 2843435
Open 5.30pm-12.30am Tues-Sat; closed Sun/Mon
Average £10.95 four courses plus coffee; house wine £9.80, glass £2
Payment A, V; TC, LV. 10% service
A family run restaurant, specialising in fish (delicious lightly battered calamari, sole) and fresh pasta - fettucine, gnocchi and warm freshly baked bread to mop up rich tomato and Alfredo sauces. Home made ice-creams are also recommended. Proprietor Ciro Geroso achieved 'Guinness Book of Records' fame for making the largest lasagne in the world at the 1990 Spring Show. The kitchen is open, so diners can see meals being prepared.

Lisa's Trattoria & Restaurant
81 Terenure Road North, Dublin 6
Tel 907469
Seating 34
Open 5pm-midnight Mon-Thurs; 5pm-1am Fri/Sat; 5pm-12.30am Sun
Average £12 ; house wine £9.50
Payment A, V; EC, LV. 10% service
A typical Italian trattoria whose specialities are spaghetti, carbonara and fettucine metro. A Venetian family-run restaurant specialising in dishes from their home city - the gnocchi is memorable. The decor is rather garish, but they do put bread sticks on the tables. Vegetarian on request.
Babies/children catered for, child portions and menu. Booking advisable. Ground floor.

Roccia Nera
5/7 Main Street, Blackrock, Co Dublin
Tel 2883347
Seating 50
Open noon-11pm seven days
Average £10; £8.50 minimum 3pm-9pm Sat/Sun; house wine Chianti £9, glass £1.95.
Payment all major credit cards except DC; EC, TC, LV.
The speciality here is A Modo Mio - quite unique fettucine. Open since 1991, it has a loyal local clientele who come for good food at an affordable price in a lively restaurant. Another open kitchen allows the diner to see what's going on behind the scenes. A good place for a bite after a browse around the Blackrock market. Sunday brunch is an interesting feature and very popular.
Babies/children catered for, child portions and menu. No smoking area (16). Booking essential Thurs and weekends. Takeaway. Ground floor.

Il Ristorante
108 Coliemore Road, Dalkey, Co Dublin
Tel 2840800
Seating 26
Open 7.30pm-10.30pm Tues-Sat; closed Sun-Mon
Average £30-35 includes wine; no house wine but list includes 65 Italian wines
Payment all major credit cards except AmEx; EC.

Despite its current popularity, this is one of the few restaurants specialising in serious modern Northern Italian cooking: home made pasta fresh every day with rich creamy sauces, and modern interpretations of traditional dishes, like the time-consuming, delicate osso bucco. An interesting wine list includes several little known but excellent Italian wines. Don't come here for spaghetti bolognese. Look for dishes like gnocchi, risotto con scampi, ravioli stuffed with crab or wild mushrooms and tagliatelle al pesto. The dining room has a clubby atmosphere while the food is excellent and decidedly up-market. A good place to celebrate an important event. Egon Ronay for last two years, member of Eurotocque. Vegetarian available.
Not wheelchair friendly. No smoking area (8). Booking advisable at weekends. Available for private parties. Smart casual dress (no t-shirts). Stairs.

La Romana
The Queens, Castle Street, Dalkey, Co Dublin
Tel 2859450
Seating 65
Open 5.30pm-11.30pm Mon-Sat; noon-10pm Sun
Average £10; £5.50 minimum after 6.30pm; house wine £10.75, glass £1.75
Payment A, V; EC, TC. 12 ½% service for eight or more.
An Italian restaurant in an Irish pub. Speciality, strangely, pesto with any type of pasta. Vegetarian available. Acceptable Italian food, at a reasonable price, in lovely Dalkey village. The Queens which is over 250 years old (est 1745) is a well-known fashionable hostelry to which city dwellers, who can afford a hefty cover charge, flock at the weekend. In the seventies and early eighties, Dalkey was Ireland's original gourmet capital and people even crossed the Liffey to dine in the fashionable hotspots under the shadow of Killiney Hill. Now one can spend a leisurely day here exploring Victoria Park, browsing through the latest literature in The Exchange Bookshop , eating in La Romana, then drinking in the Queens surrounded by charming historical ambience with lots of bric a brac.
Babies/children catered for up to 8.30pm, child portions and menu; high chairs. No smoking area (15). Function room upstairs for parties of 45+. Takeaway. Ground floor.

San Marino
77 Dame Street, Dublin 2
Tel 6792403
Seating 54
Open 6pm-1am seven days
Average £13; £16 set dinner; house wine £9.50
Payment all major credit cards; EC. 10% service.
San Marino is situated beside the Olympia Theatre, facing Dublin Castle - a corner of Dublin well served by Italian restaurants. Decorated in tones of blue, and dominated by a Victorian figurine which serves as a fountain, the overall chic impression is enhanced by pink candles on the tables. Well-situated for pre- or post-theatre dining, prices seem to be slightly below average. A pianist provides weekend entertainment. Speciality is tagiatelle al salmone, or veal. Vegetarian available.
Babies/children catered for up to 7pm, child portions; baby changing room. No smoking area (12). Booking advisable. Smart casual dress. Ground floor. Stairs to toilets.

Unicorn Restaurant
12c Merrion Court, Merrion Row, Dublin 2
Tel 6688552/6762182
Seating 70
Average £12 ; £7 minimum at all times; house wine £9.20
Payment A, V; EC, TC.
Italian restaurant that is very much a cult place, particularly patronised by those who want to be seen amongst the intelligentsia (as well as the intelligensia themselves). Conveniently located a few steps from the Shelbourne Hotel's Horseshoe Bar, it is also a favourite with the Shelbourne's philosophy set. The decor was probably the height of fashion in the early seventies but it has worn to a patina that almost gives it the charm of nostalgia. The food, though genuine Italian home cooking, is not at all exceptional. It is

the atmosphere, the crowded room, the possibility of rubbing shoulders with another James Joyce, that give the Unicorn its appeal, especially Saturday at lunchtime. Speciality is homemade pasta. Vegetarian avalable.
Babies/children catered for, child portions and menu. Wheelchair friendly booked in advance. No smoking area (8). Booking advisable (especially lunch). Ground floor.

Il Gabbiano Restaurant
8 South Great Georges Street, Dublin 2
Tel 6793629/6777289
Seating 50
Open 6pm-12.30am Mon-Sat
Average £15; £6.75 minimum; £18.95 table d'hote; house wine £10.95.
Payment all major credit cards; EC, TC.
10% service.
Piano and singer provide weekend entertainment. Specialities are fresh fish, veal and pasta. Vegetarian on request.
Babies/children allowed early evening. No smoking area (6). Booking advisable. Can be booked for private parties. Neat casual dress. Ground floor.

Le Caprice
12 St Andrews Street, Dublin 2
Tel 6794050/6773333
Seating 150
Open 6pm-12.30pm seven days
Average £15 dinner; house wine £9.50
Payment all major credit cards; EC, TC, LV.
12% service.
International food with an Italian emphasis with veal, fish and game on the wide ranging menu. Entertainment is constituted by a piano with occasional singer on Saturday nights and a disco downstairs. A favourite post-theatre spot during the opera season, it is a haunt of visiting tenors. Received an award from the Academy of Italian Cuisine which tests the standards of Italian cuisine outside Italy. Speciality is fresh prawns alla Italiana. Vegetarian available.
Babies/children catered for, child portions. Not wheelchair friendly, stairs to lower dining room. Booking advisable. Private parties (minimum 20) catered for. Ground floor. Stairs down.

Il Primo
16 Montague Street, Dublin 2
Tel 4783373
Seating 45
Open noon-3pm Mon; noon-3pm, 6pm-11pm Tues-Sat
Average £15; £5 special lunch; house wine per litre £10.
Payment all major credit cards; EC, LV.
Tucked away in a little alley off Harcourt Street, this is definitely a fashion-conscious restaurant, serving interesting homemade pasta and excellent sauces, as well as pizzas with superior inventive toppings. Abuzz for lunch with businessmen from various neighbouring accountancy firms, in the evening it is frequented by couples on their way to the Concert Hall, which is just around the corner. Although the cooking is original, and better than average, it is not a first league gourmet restaurant and I would have loved more brandy in my tiramisu. Vegetarian available.
Babies/children catered for, child portions. Not wheelchair friendly. No smoking area (12). Booking advisable. Takeaway. Ground floor. Stairs.

Nico's Restaurant
53 Dame Street, Dublin 2
Tel 6773062
Seating 50
Open 12.30pm-2.30pm Mon-Fri; 6pm-12.30 Mon-Sat.
Average £15; £6.50 lunch; house wine £9.50.
Payment all major credit cards; EC, TC.
10% service pm only.
Although the exterior of this Italian restaurant is not particularly prepossessing, flowers on the table, heavy velvet drapes and crisp linen make the interior very smart. Lunch prices range from £5.95 - cannelloni and salad - to £7.50 for soup, scampi fritter, chips and coffee. The emphasis of the à la carte dinner menu is on homemade pasta for £5.95. Fish, too, is of interest particularly if your budget or credit card is a little more elastic. Desserts, of the Italian variety, include favourites like cassata and zabaglione. Nico's menu reminds the visitor that 'A meal without wine is like a day

without sunshine'. Speciality is homemade pasta. Vegetarian available.
Babies/children catered for, child portions. No smoking area (8). Booking advisable. Smart casual dress. Ground floor. Stairs to toilets.

Kapriol Restaurant
45 Lower Camden Street, Dublin 2
Tel 4751235/2985496
Seating 30
Open 7.30pm-midnight Mon-Sat
Average £30; house wine £10.50.
Payment all major credit cards, EC, TC.
12½% service
Kapriol takes its name from a gin-like liqueur from Corregliano Veneto between Venice and the Alps in the Italian provence of Treviso, the original home of the Peruzzi family, owners of the restaurant. A traditional Italian menu features fish and veal dishes. Rather expensive and served in a quaint Irish/Italian manner, the food is nonetheless of infinite good quality and not meant to be hurried. Specialities are Prawns Kapriol (expect huge prawns!) and turbot. Vegetarian available.
Babies/children catered for, child portions. No smoking area (8). Booking essential. Ground floor. Stairs to toilets.

Giovanini Pizzeria Restaurant
Townyard Lane, Malahide, Co Dublin
Tel 8451733
Seating 45
Open 12.30pm-midnight seven days
Average £8.50; house wine £8.75, glass £1.95.
Payment all major credit cards except AmEx; EC, TC
A fun Italian restaurant, with lots of tables pushed together, transports you away to an exotic foreign location. Certainly, the prices are right, so with a liberal dousing of house wine you can easily perpetrate this illusion. The Italian menu goes beyond pizza to pasta, chicken and meat. Speciality though is pasta. Vegetarian available.
Babies/children catered for, child portions; high chairs. No smoking area (8). Booking advisable. Takeaway. Ground floor.

Bernardo's Restaurant
19 Lincoln Place, Dublin 2
Tel 6762471
Seating 50
Open 12.30pm-2.45pm Mon-Fri; 6pm-12.30am Mon-Sat; closed Sun and bank holidays.
Average £15; minimum .35p; £15.95 set meals; house wine £8.95 (Valpolicella and Soave)
Payment all major credit cards; EC, TC
10% service with dinner.
Established in 1954 and situated close to Merrion Square and Trinity College, Bernardo's is Dublin's oldest Italian restaurant, and, according to an interview prior to taking office in 1991, is now President Mary Robinson's favourite eating place. In fact, her pre-inauguration party was held here . They make their own pasta, including organic spinach ravioli. Deep-fried scampi with a hint of garlic is served with a mixed side salad. No batter coatings here! Desserts include tiramisu or homemade cassata. The service is brisk, perhaps rather too brisk, but then it was lunchtime. A convenient little Italian restaurant. Speciality is scampi al Bernardo.

BERNARDO
19 RESTAURANT 19
19 Lincoln place. Dublin 2. Phone: 6762471.
We cater for parties - birthdays. communions. private. etc..

Vegetarian available.
Babies/children catered for, child portions. Wheelchair friendly (except the toilets). No smoking area (15). Booking advisable. Takeaway by arrangement. Ground floor. Stairs.

Pasta Pasta
27 Exchequer Street, Dublin 2
Tel 6792565
Seating 55-60
Open noon-12.30am Mon-Sat; 6pm-11.30pm Sun
Average £15; £6 set lunch; house wine £9.90.
Payment all major credit cards; EC, LV.
Pasta Pasta is run by Joe and Luisa Aprile who serve food, as befits their origins, from southern Italy. The speciality is homemade pasta with interesting sauces which Luisa herself has invented. Al Salmone contains smoked salmon, garlic, olive oil and a hint of cream. Pesto alla Genovese - fresh basil, garlic, olive oil, pine kernels and Parmesan cheese - is served with a generous mixed side salad. From a rather selective dessert menu, tiramisu comes in a large portion. Pizzas are another feature of this bright, airy restaurant and, for the more health conscious, Pasta Pasta offers a fine selection of Mediterranean salads. Good value for money in pleasant unpretentious surroundings. Vegetarian available
Babies/children catered for, child portions; high chairs. Wheelchair friendly (except toilets). No smoking area (25). Booking advisable, essential at weekends. Takeaway.

Casa Pasta
12 Harbour Road, Howth, Co Dublin
Tel 393823/390567
Seating 45
Open 12.30pm-2.30pm (seasonal); 6pm-11.30pm seven days
Average £9; house wine £8.50.
Payment all major credit cards except DC,EC, TC, LV. 15% service for six or more.
Howth's new pasta restaurant is small and intimate, with tables close together, so be prepared to talk to your neighbours. Entertainment consists of Hungarian music on Thursday as well as sporadic other nights. The open kitchen makes it possible to see your meal in the making. The bar/kitchen space is cleverly designed to resemble a boat. Although described as Italian, the menu is an interesting mix of international dishes. Specialities include pasta and salad. Vegetarian available.
Babies/children catered for, child portions, high chairs. Not wheelchair friendly. No smoking area (8). Booking advisable. Stairs.

Luigi's Restaurant
2a Main Street, Raheny, Dublin 5
Tel 316395
Open noon-2.30pm Mon-Fri; 5pm-11.30pm Mon-Sat; noon-10pm Sun
Average £10; £5.50 lunch noon-2.30; house wine £8
Payment A, V; EC, TC
This restaurant, with an American touch, is Raheny's principal restaurant, and interestingly, is the old school house dating back 210 years. As a result, there is a cottage feel with floral tablecloths, red overcovers and matching chairs giving a bright, cheerful look. Featured on the menu is a bolognese burger and crostini - crisp French bread with a tomato and mozarella sauce. Desserts include warm raspberries with ice-cream. Specialities are steaks, pizza and pasta. Vegetarian on request.
Babies/children catered for, child portions and menu; high chairs. Not wheelchair friendly. No smoking area (8). Booking advisable at weekends. Tables outdoors. Private room for parties. Takeaway by request. Ground floor. Stairs.

Cafe Caruso
47 South William Street, Dublin 2
Tel 6770708/6717017
Seating 80
Open 6pm-12.15 am seven days; 6pm-11.15 pm Sun
Average £16.00; £8.50 three courses pre-theatre; house wine selection £9.95. Fully licensed.
Payment all major credit cards; EC, TC
Caruso boasts an Italian-directed menu, which is popularly priced. After a major social occasion, it is common to spy many well-known

faces dining and carousing to the tinkling of background piano - one highly controversial columnist even keeps her own table by the front door. The Italian cuisine is authentic, the pasta excellent, desserts are flavoursome (especially the ice creams) and the wine menu international. The decor is rich and inspiring and the overall sense of abundance and well-being is hard to suppress when Caruso is on song.
Babies/children allowed. Not wheelchair friendly. No smoking area (26). Booking advisable. Private room for parties of 40. Neat casual dress. Ground floor. Stairs to toilets.

La Finezza Restaurant
above Kiely's Pub, Donnybrook, Dublin 4
Tel 2693606
Seating 125
Open 5.30pm-11.30pm Mon-Sat;
5.30pm-10pm Sun.
Average £15; house wine £9.50. Fully licensed.
Payment A, V; EC, TC. 10% service for ten or more.
La Finezza, as Italian as it sounds, is perched over Kiely's Pub on Donnybrook's main drag. Attended by a regular clientele from surrounding districts, there is always a generous activitiy and bustle about the place. The menu is most notable for its pizza and pasta dishes which are very reliable. Very often frequented by large parties who avail of their long regency banquettes and white swathed tables, this is, nonetheless, not to deter couples or single diners who value private savouring. Straw coloured, Duval-Leroi Restaurant of the Year for 1992, and with a full licence, many other restaurants are sweeping their floors when Finezza is still in full flow.
Babies/children catered for, child portions. Not wheelchair friendly. No smoking area (16). Booking advisable. Tables outdoors. Private room for parties. Neat casual dress. Stairs.

Da Vicenzo
133 Upper Leeson Street, Dublin 4
Tel 6609906
Seating 56
Open 12.30pm-11.45pm Mon-Sat; 1pm-10pm Sun

Average £13; £5.90 minimum lunch; set price meals for large parties on request; house wine £8.50.
Payment all major credit cards; EC, LV.
An unfussy Italian trattoria around the block from the Burlington - a block now housing such joyspots as Cafe Java and Senor Sassi's at the foot of Leeson Street Bridge. The not quite navy blue is the dominating decor feature as it assails you at every turn. Possessed of a miniscule snug of a lounge seat just inside the door, the restaurant downstairs is bustly and small. Starters are, by and large, appetising at around £2.50 while main courses average out at about £9. The menu is very imaginative and remarkably well presented. Bread is not always the freshest and service is on the slow side - not necessarily a bad thing. Good for a down-at-heel romantic tryst, worthwhile pizza and, if slightly cheaper, I'd say a real find. Specialities are pizzas and pastas. Vegetarian available.
Babies/children catered for, child portions; high chairs available. Wheelchair friendly (except toilets). No smoking area (6). Booking advisable, essential at weekends. Takeaway by arrangement.

Pacino's
18 Suffolk Street, Dublin 2
Tel 6775651
Seating 70
Open noon-11pm Mon-Sat; closed Sun.
Average £8.50; £3.95 set lunch noon-2pm; £4 minimum after 6pm; house wine £6.95.
Payment A, V; EC, LV.
An Italian ristorante, Pacino's is very centrally located. The tiled floor and bare wooden tables give the impression of a local trattoria in some North Italian town. The à la carte dinner menu includes steak, burgers and chicken. Restaurants of a reasonable price and high standard are hard to find, so check this one out. Specialities are pizza, pasta and steaks. Vegetarian available.
Babies/children catered for, child portions and menu; high chairs. Wheelchair friendly (except toilets). No smoking area (35). Ground floor. Stairs to toilets.

La Tavola Restaurant
114 Rock Road, Booterstown, Co Dublin
Tel 2835101
Seating 30
Open 4.30pm-11.30pm Mon-Sat; closed Sun
Average £11; house wine £8.95
Payment all major credit cards except DC, EC.
Small Italian pizza restaurant with open kitchen close to Blackrock DART station. The All'Arabbiata is really piquant. Speciality is spaghetti carbonara. Vegetarian available.
Babies/children catered for, child portions. No smoking area (8). Booking advisable at weekends. Ground floor. Step.

Trattoria da Mario
39 Ranelagh, Dublin 6
Tel 972078
Seating 55
Open noon-11pm Sun-Thurs; noon-midnight Fri/Sat
Average £9-10; £3.95 lunch special two courses; house wine £7.95
Payment A, V; EC
An Italian country kitchen layout with open hearth and old pine furniture where the

emphasis is very much on a relaxed atmosphere - absolutely no bookings taken and very informal. At peak times, customers are despatched across to Russell's pub to be summoned when the table is ready. Vegetarian on request.

Babies/children catered for, kiddies' special menu. Not wheelchair friendly. No smoking area (6). Takeaway. Ground floor. Stairs to toilets.

Oriental

Chinese restaurateurs won their spurs in Ireland by being among the hardest working of all the catering corps. In any backwoods corner where the sidewalks were rolled up at sundown, the hungry and the hungover could be sure to find a late-night Chineser dispensing hot quickly prepared meals.

Shift-workers and other night owls were connaisseurs of spring rolls, barbecued spare ribs and chop suey in an era when meat and two veg were the dining-out norm. Understandably, early Chinese caterers modified traditional dishes to Irish tastes and there were chips - often very good ones - with everything.

The influx of Hong Kong Chinese in the seventies opened the horizons to an increasingly sophisticated approach to Chinese food and more user friendly surroundings presided over by smiling proprietors. Dubliners began to appreciate the difference between Szechuan and Cantonese and were charmed by artful presentations in lacy edible baskets with carved fresh pineapples and pleated stuffed dim sum dumplings.

Although oriental food in Dublin is dominated by Chinese, there is a new sprinkling of Malaysian and Thai restaurants, with a following among holiday makers to those climes. Akiko Hoashi remains sole purveyor of Japanese cuisine in Ayumi-Ya which has recently expanded into the city centre and offers Dublin's choicest designer takeaways in smart banto-boxes.

Good World Restaurant
18 South Great Georges Street, Dublin 2
Tel 6775373
Seating 80
Open noon -3am seven days
Average £5.50 lunch; £13.50 minimum dinner; house wine £8.50.
Payment all major credit cards; EC, TC.
10% service

A Chinese restaurant worth visiting just because it does not have the standard ubiquitous Chinese interior design. It also has excellent authentic food and a large oriental clientele - always a good sign. There is a standard menu, but to really experience the excellence of the food, do order from the dim sum menu - try a mix of steamed and fried dishes but ideally go with a group to make the most of the wide range on offer.
Babies/children catered for; high chairs. Wheelchair friendly (except toilets). No smoking area (12). Booking advisable. Private parties (up to 20) catered for. Takeaway by arrangement. Ground floor. Stairs.

China China
71-72 South Great Georges Street, Dublin 2
Tel 4750338
Seating 100
Open 12-2.30pm Mon-Fri; 6pm-midnight Mon-Thurs; 6pm-1am Fri-Sat; 2pm-11.30pm Sun.
Average £11.50; £6 lunch; house wine £9.
Payment all major credit cards; EC, LV.
10% service.

Fairly recently opened in place of another Chinese, Pearl City, China China (so good they named it twice!!) is the property of ex - Londoner Stephen Lau who has spent many years plying his trade in that metropolis. The menu is a mix of Szechuan, Peking and Cantonese. Usual extensive menu and reputed claims to house the largest restaurant fountain in Dublin!
Babies/children catered for, child portions. Wheelchair friendly (except toilets). No smoking area (34). Booking advisable. Air conditioned. Private parties up to 60. Takeaway by arrangement.

Jazz Chinese Restaurant
Beech Park Avenue, Coolock Village Shopping Centre, Dublin 5
Tel 8474011/8473344
Seating 60
Open 6pm-12.30pm Mon-Thurs; 6pm-1am Fri-Sat; 6pm-midnight Sun.
Average £11; set price meals from £11; house wine £8.

Payment all major credit cards; EC, TC.
10% service.
This looks like so many other Chinese restaurants but prices seem below average. Specialising in Peking and Szechuan cuisine, a real treat is its special platter served in intricately designed Chinese ceramic dishes comprising spare ribs, spring roll, prawn crackers and prawn and sesame toast. For service, presentation and price this restaurant scores high marks. Worth a visit if you are in the area. Moreover, they also have a secure car park.
Babies/children catered for; high chairs. Not wheelchair friendly. No smoking area (12). Booking advisable. Private parties catered for. Takeaway, delivery. Stairs.

Pagoda Restaurant
Sutton Cross Shopping Centre, Sutton, Dublin 13
Tel 390218
Seating 56
Open 6.30pm-11.30pm seven days; 12.30pm-2.30pm Sun.

Average £18.50; set price meals from £15; house wine £9.
Payment all major credit cards; EC, LV.
10% service.
Babies/children catered for, child portions and menu; high chairs. Not wheelchair friendly. No smoking area (10). Booking advisable. Ground floor. Stairs.

Furama
Anglesea House, Donnybrook, Dublin 4
Tel 2830522/260036
Seating 100
Open 12.30pm-2pm Mon-Fri; 6.pm-11.30pm Mon-Thurs; 6pm-midnight Fri/Sat; 1.30pm-11pm Sun
Average £20; £10 minimum; house wine £8. Spirits, liqueurs available.
Payment all major credit cards; EC, TC.
10% service.
The word 'Furama' translated from Chinese equates 'wealthy, beautiful and elegant' and begs the question whether these are prerequisites for admission, especially when faced with a daunting black door and golden bell. Upon entry, you pass through the small lounge and cross the Bridge of Wisdom over the fountain (water signifying luck in China) to enter the dining area - and we thought the Irish were superstitious! The decor, as you'd expect, is rich, while the leatherbound menu has won an award for its presentation. Staff are highly polished and the food is exemplary, in particular the seafood. With Chinese patrons regularly in attendance, the hint should be taken.
Babies/children catered for (early/Sunday family lunch), child portions. No smoking area (20). Booking advisable. Air conditioned (refrigerated). Ground floor.

Fans Cantonese Restaurant
60 Dame Street, Dublin 2
Tel 6794263
Seating 100
Open 12.30pm-2.30pm, 6pm-12.30am Mon-Fri; 12.30pm-12.30 am Fri/Sat.
Average £12; £6 minimum charge 12.30pm-2.30pm; house wine £9.

Payment all major credit cards; EC, TC, LV.
Cantonese restaurant where the speciality is aromatic duck. Stephen Fan is the owner of Kites in Ballsbridge and Fans is the city-centre off-shoot with a similar ambience and slightly lower prices. On the extensive lunch menu, two price structures, either £6 or £8, are determined by the main course. For example, duck would be £8. For dinner, the combination platter consists of spare ribs, sesame toast and a pancake roll - a filling starter as the pancake roll is jam packed with bean sprouts and tiny shrimps. Very nice.
Babies/children catered for; child menu; high chairs. Wheelchair friendly (except toilets). No smoking area (12). Booking advisable. Takeaway. Ground floor access.

Prince Restaurant
112 Middle Abbey Street, Dublin 1
Tel 6727917
Seating 44
Open noon-9pm Mon-Sat, closed Sun.
Average £10; £5 minimum evenings; £10 set price four courses; £6 three courses 6pm-9pm; house wine £8.60, glass £1.60.
Payment A, V; EC, LV, TC.
10% service 6pm-9pm.
Cantonese restaurant. Vegetarian on request.
Babies/children catered for, child portions. Wheelchair friendly (except toilets). No smoking area (12). Booking advisable. Takeaway. Ground floor. Stairs to toilets.

Royal Garden Chinese Restaurant
Westbury Centre, 30 Clarendon Street, Dublin 2
Tel 6716997
Seating 70
Open 12.30pm-2.30pm, 6pm-midnight Mon-Fri; 12.30pm-midnight Sat/Sun.
Average £11; £5.50 minimum; £15 set five courses; house wine £9.
Payment all major credit cards; EC, TC.
12½% service.
A large but chic Chinese restaurant located at the side of the Westbury Centre with its entrance on Clarendon Street. Pastel green walls, high-backed chairs and open screens make it a comfortable place, somewhat or a departure from traditional Chinese restaurant decor. Cantonese / Szechuan cuisine with specialities like steamed sole and steamed prawn with garlic sauce. Vegetarian available.
Babies/children catered for, high chairs. Wheelchair friendly (except toilets). No smoking area (16). Booking advisable. Takeaway by arrangement. Ground floor. Stairs to toilets.

Ruby King
13 Wexford Street, Dublin 2
Tel 47882268
Seating 38
Open 5.30pm-1.30am seven days; noon-2.30pm Thurs- Fri.
Average £11; £13 set price meal; house wine £9.
Payment all major credit cards; EC, LV.
10% service.
Wexford Street's only Chinese restaurant has an extensive takeaway menu. An average takeaway works out about £4. The restaurant has recently changed hands and the new chef who has introduced a selection of Szechuan dishes, will produce if requested, any dish - within reason. A favourite after closing time but before that, you will be sure of a table.
Babies/children allowed up to 8pm. No smoking area (14). Takeaway. Ground floor access.

Chanze Chinese Restaurant
7 St Andrew's Street, Dublin 2
Tel 6792988
Seating 30
Open 12.30pm-2.30pm, 5.30pm-12.30am Mon-Fri; 12.30pm-1am Sat; 5pm-midnight Sun.
Average £15 ; £5.50 lunch; £7.50pre-theatre; house wine £9.50.
Payment all major credit cards; EC, LV, TC.
10% service.
Cantonese/Szechuan restaurant where the Chinese decor is played down. Speciality is chicken in a bird's nest, fillet of beef in chef's special sauce. Liam Hurley must be the first Irish Chinese restaurant proprietor. By profession a musician, he teamed up with a Chinese to start the restaurant in 1987.
Deep fried ice-cream comes batter covered

ensuring the inside is not just a melted mess. The service is prompt and efficient. A Chinese restaurant with a hint of nouvelle cuisine.
Babies/children catered for, child portions. Wheelchair friendly (except toilets). No smoking area (6). Booking advisable weekends. Free delivery within four miles, thereafter 50p a mile. Ground floor. Stairs and lift.

Silks Restaurant
The Moorings, 1 The Mall, Malahide, Co Dublin
Tel 8453331
Seating 75
Open 6pm-12.30pm seven days; 12.30pm-2.30pm Sunday lunch
Average £15 ; £10 minimum; house wine £8.95.
Payment all major credit cards; EC, £10, LV.
10% service.
Silks is renowned in Malahide for good food, a comfortable atmosphere and friendly staff. The menu is mainly Cantonese but there is also a touch of Szechuan and Peking.
Babies/children catered for lunchtime and early evening, high chairs. No smoking area (30). Booking advisable. Air conditioned. Takeaway by arrangement. Ground floor access.

China Palace Restaurant
120 Ranelagh, Dublin 6
Tel 9799452
Seating 60
Open 12.30pm-2.15pm Wed-Fri; 6pm-12.30am seven days.
Average £12 ; four course lunch from £5; £16 set price meal; house wine £9.50.
Payment all major credit cards; EC, TC, LV.
10% service
This restaurant in Ranelagh is deceptively small but there are in fact two floors with predominantly black and grey decor. The Cantonese/Szechuan menu features specialities like duckling and other hot and spicy Chinese dishes. Vegetarian is widely available
Babies/children allowed; baby changing room. Wheelchair friendly (except toilets). No smoking area (14). Booking advisable. Private parties catered for. Takeaway by arrangement. Ground floor. Stairs.

Singapore Gardens
Main Street, Dundrum, Dublin 14
Tel 2983911/ 2988880
Seating 100
Open 12.30-2pm, 6pm-11pm Sun-Thurs; until 11.30pm Fri/Sat.
Average £15 ; £4.95 lunch; house wine £9.50.
Fully licensed.
Payment A, V; EC, TC, LV.
New venture by Wexford Co. with restaurants outside Dublin (Wexford mainly), opened July 1992 with large off-street car park. Tastefully decorated Chinese restaurant uses striking table colour contrast - mint tablecovers/pale pink cloth napkins. Red brick walls with two open hearths mixed with darkwood stairs, bar and panelling combine with food of excellent standard. The restaurant specialises in Singapore dishes (spicy and hot) but places equal emphasis on its European menu. Seafood dish (prawns and scallops) with spring onions and fresh ginger (£9.50) as generous as the space

between tables. Eager to please but not over-intrusive service.
Babies/children catered for, child portions; high chairs. Booking advisable. Second floor. Stairs and lift.

Legend Restaurant
21 Main Street, Blackrock, Co Dublin
Tel 2835957
Seating 36
Open 5.30pm-midnight Sun-Thurs; 5.30pm-11.30pm weekends.
Average £16; house wine £8.50.
Payment all major credit cards except DC; EC, TC. 10% service.
Blackrock is rapidly taking over from Dalkey as Dublin's foody village and Chinese cuisine, as the origin of all civilised eating, is naturally represented. The speciality here is ping poon platter (combinations of spring roll, baked prawn, ribs and warm wanton), but the menu gives the friendly invitation "If there is anything you would like, not listed on the menu, please let us know." Decorated in the usual sophisticated oriental style, beloved of up-market Chinese restaurants, it provides quite a good venue for a special night out.
Babies/children catered for by special arrangement. Not wheelchair friendly. No smoking area (8). Booking advisable. Private parties up to 50. Takeaway. Ground floor. Stairs.

Kites Restaurant
17 Ballsbridge Terrace, Dublin 4
Tel 6607415
Seating 60
Open 12.30pm-2pm Mon-Fri; 6.30pm-11.30 pm seven days.
Average £17; £12 lunch; £18.50 table d'hote; house wine £9.80.
Payment all major credit cards; EC, TC.
10% service
This little restaurant, overlooking the Dodder, has built up a reputation for classical Cantonese cooking that is a little beyond the ordinary. Specialities include lobster with ginger and spring onion on a black bean sauce and stir fry dishes in potato baskettes. Although comparatively

expensive, its original menu and excellent cooking put it in the top league of Chinese restaurants. The decor comprises painted mirrors with Chinese motifs, depicting an idealised but nonetheless awe-inspiring China. There is an unusual raised dining area in the centre of the restaurant. At lunchtime it is busy with businessmen, but in the evening there is a fair proportion of couples celebrating an evening out.
Wheelchair friendly (except toilets). No smoking area (10). Booking advisable. Private parties catered for. Ground floor. Stairs to toilets.

Wings Chinese & Seafood Restaurant
5 Windsor Terrace, Sandycove, Co Dublin
Tel 2804600
Seating 80
Open 6pm-12.30am Mon-Thurs; noon-2pm, 6pm-1am Fri/Sat; noon-midnight Sun.
Average £15.50 including glass of wine; £8.50 minimum 12.30pm-4.30pm Sun.
Payment all major credit cards; EC, TC.
10% service
The speciality of this sea-front restaurant, which stands on the site of the former "Digbys", is naturally, a seafood set dinner. As the food came to our table, I was reminded of that ancient Chinese proverb "A good meal is eaten first with the eyes, then the nose and finally the mouth". The five course Sunday lunch is good value. The complimentary glass of wine is a nice extra with the set dinner. The upstairs dining room has a spectacular view across Dublin Bay to Howth Head. Book a table in the bay window!
Babies/children catered for, child menu and portions; high chairs and baby changing facilities. Booking advisable weekends and public holidays. Private parties up to 50. Takeaway by arrangement. Ground floor. Stairs to upper dining room.

Empress
Clifton Avenue, Monkstown, Co Dublin
Tel 2643188
Seating 80
Open 12.30-2pm, 6pm-12 midnight Thurs-Sat; 12.30pm-11pm Sun.
Average £16.50 four courses (set meal); house wine £10.50.
Payment all major credit cards; TC.
10% service
Thai and Cantonese restaurant specialising in Shantung and Thai cuisine. Their noodles are freshly made in front of the diner, an entertainment in itself. Lobster with sweet basil at £16 is a dish for a special occassion. The baked chicken Portuguese style is obviously a throwback to ancient explorers of the Orient. The decoration is very plush with a black and white colour scheme and a lot of gold and silver plate. An opulent centre piece in the dining room is a large ship carved out of jade, imported by the owner from Peking.
Not wheelchair friendly.

Logan's
3 Temple Rd, Blackrock, Co Dublin
Tel 2836199
Seating 40
Open 12.30-2.15pm Mon-Fri; 6pm-midnight Sun-Thurs, 6pm-1am Fri-Sat.
Average £13; £6.95 minimum Sun-Thurs 6pm-7pm; house wine £8.75.
Payment all major credit cards; EC, LV, TC.
10% service.
Malaysian/Chinese restaurant with a speciality of satay and oriental chicken and prawn fingers. A good version of aromatic duck is also served. The only fault was that the portions were too big! Logan is from Ipoh in Malaysia so do expect the real thing and don't be put off by the decor. The house special is oriental chicken fingers, slender portions of chicken in crispy batter, served with a chilli sauce. Quite delicious and not a bit like "Captain Birdseye"!
Babies/children catered for, child portions. No smoking area (6). Booking advisable weekends. Takeaway. Ground floor.

China Sichuan Restaurant
4 Lower Kilmacud Road, Stillorgan, Co. Dublin
Tel 2884817
Seating 50
Open 12.30pm-2.30pm, 6pm-11pm Mon-Fri; 6pm-11pm Sat; 1pm-2.30pm, 6pm-11pm Sun.
Average £15.50; £16.50 set five course meal; house wine £8.50.
Payment all major credit cards except DC; EC, LV, TC. 10% service
Smoked duckling is a Sichuan (also spelt Szechuan) speciality as is the monkfish with cashew nuts. Spiced bean curd (soya bean milk curdled with vinegar) is another favourite of the house. Allegedly, this is the only genuine Sichuan restaurant in Dublin and is supplied by the Sichuan Food Company in Chengdu, the capital of Sichuan province. Traditionally Sichuan food is hot and spicy, but to suit local taste Mr Hui has compromised with some of his dishes. For a piquant flavour start with "hot and sour soup" - a peppery mixture of chicken, beancurd, crispy noodles and soya bean. It might get your sinuses but gives a good indication of some of the flavours typical of Sichuan cookery. An interesting eating experience.
Babies/children allowed. Wheelchair friendly (except toilets). Booking esential weekends. Parties catered for. Ground floor.

Golden Carp Chinese Restaurant
5 Pembroke Cottages, Ballinteer Road, Dundrum, Dublin 14
Tel 2980654
Seating 45
Open noon - 2.30 pm, 6.30pm-midnight seven days.
Average £5.50 lunch; £12.50 dinner; house wine £9.
Payment all major credit cards except AmEx; EC, TC. 10% service
A small Chinese restaurant tucked away beside Dundrum Bowl. Although the decor is rather typical "Chinese restaurant", prices are more reasonable than most. Cantonese cuisine is probably the best known to Westerners, because of the huge emigration in the 19th century, as well as Europe's long association with Southern China for smuggling opium from the late 18th century. Green peppers stuffed with prawn with a soya based sauce is a typical Cantonese dish.
Babies/children allowed. Not wheelchair friendly. No smoking area (10). Takeaway. Ground floor. Stairs.

Pings Restaurant
The Grove, Stillorgan, Co Dublin
Tel 2831373
Seating 68
Open 6pm-11.45pm Thurs-Sun; noon-2.30pm seven days.
Average £18; £9.30 lunch; house wine £9.50.
Payment all major credit cards; EC, TC. 10% service
The speciality of this Cantonese restaurant is fresh lobster with ginger and spring onion or seasoned and spicy, and soft shell crab served as an appetiser. Seafood dominates the menu, though there are also some of the old favourites like shredded beef on a sizzling platter (£9.50) and lemon chicken (£8.50). A most strangely named dish is "Beancurd with Eight Precious Gems", the gems being mixed meats and seafood. Unusually for a Chinese restaurant there is nightly entertainment in the form of a pianist. The dining area, from which the diner can see his food being prepared in the open plan kitchen, is dominated by a huge artificial tree.
Babies/children allowed early evening only. Not wheelchair friendly. No smoking area (12). Booking advisable. Takeaway by arrangement. Ground floor. Stairs.

Imperial Chinese Restaurant
12A Wicklow Street, Dublin 2
Tel 6772580
Seating 100
Open 12.30pm - 12.30am seven days.
Average £15-£18; £6 three course lunch; house wine £8.95.
Payment all major credit cards except DC; EC, TC. 10% service
The Imperial is famous for its Cantonese dim-sum (one of only two in Dublin). There is a choice of about 40 dishes and the

adventurous diner can have a great experience here. This traditional Oriental brunch is especially popular with Dublin's Chinese community on a Sunday. This is a well-established restaurant with a good reputation for authentic cuisine.
Babies/children catered for; high chairs. Wheelchair friendly (except toilets). No smoking area (10). Booking advisable. Private parties up to 50 catered for. Takeaway by arrangement. Ground floor. Stairs.

The Wok Inn
17A Lower Baggot Street, Dublin 2
Tel 6762050
Seating 34
Open noon-2.30pm Mon-Fri; 6pm-11.45pm Mon-Sat; 6pm-11.30pm Sun.
Average £12; lunch from £5.95; dinner from £7; house wine £9.95.
Payment all major credit cards; EC, TC.
10% service
Located close to Quinnsworth in Lower Baggot Street, the ambience is most definitely oriental with bamboo chairs and black-topped tables. For under a tenner choose one of the prawn dishes such as king prawn with green pepper and black bean sauce or king prawn with cashew nuts. In the evening, though smart for a night out, it is cheap enough to be a good place for meal just because you are hungry!
Babies/children allowed. Not wheelchair friendly. No smoking area (10). Booking advisable. Takeaway by arrangement. Ground floor. Stairs.

Ming Court
17 Dame Street, Dublin 2
Tel 6792710
Seating 100
Open 12.30pm-2pm, 6pm-12.30am Tues-Fri; 5.30pm-1am Sat; 2pm-midnight Sun; closed Mon except bank holiday weekends.
Average £14; £5.90-6.90 lunch; house wine £8.50.
Payment all major credit cards; EC, TC.
10% service
Chinese/Malaysian restaurant whose specialities include yuk song - minced pork with rice noodles in iceberg lettuce, Singapore noodles and aromatic duck. Malayasian cuisine is heavily influenced by China, but tends to be slightly spicier, with elements similar to Thai cooking, which is just to the north.
Babies/children allowed. Wheelchair friendly (except toilets). No smoking area (10). Booking advisable at weekends. Takeaway. Ground floor. Stairs.

Kingsland (Dalkey) Chinese Restaurant
24 Castle Street, Dalkey, Co Dublin
Tel 285 0647
Seating 100
Open 5.30pm-12.45am Tues-Sat; 4pm-midnight Sun; closed Mon.
Average £14; £13 set price meal ; house wine £8.75.
Payment all major credit cards except DC; EC.
10% service.
This restaurant bravely claims to specialise in everything Szechuan and Cantonese and to provide the diner with a sizzling experience in oriental cuisine. Hidden away in Dalkey's main street it is a comfortable upstairs eatery, though the stairs might be a deterrent for some. The menu is traditional Chinese, but it is a pleasant place in this fashionable village (home to Hugh Leonard and once to George Bernard Shaw) for supper after a brisk walk over Killiney Hill.
Babies/children allowed. Not wheelchair friendly. No smoking area (40). Booking advisable at weekends. Air conditioned. Ground floor. Stairs.

Mr. Hungs
5A The Crescent, Monkstown, Co Dublin
Tel 2843365/2843982
Seating 85
Open 6pm-12.30am Mon-Sat; 12.30pm-2.30 Fri/Sat; 1pm-midnight Sun.
Average £15; £10.95 set lunch; £16 dinner; house wine £9
Payment all major credit cards; EC, TC.
10% service
Specialising in Sezechaun and Cantonese cuisine, the speciality here is duck, particularly crispy aromatic duck. This is

one of the best known and most fashionable of all oriental restaurants. Vegetarian on request.
Babies/children catered for; high chairs. No smoking area (30). Booking advisable. Takeaway. Neat casual dress. Ground floor. Stairs.

Zen Chinese Restaurant
89 Upper Rathmines Road, Dublin 6
Tel 979428
Seating 100
Open 6pm-midnight seven days; 12.30pm-2pm Thurs-Sun.
Average £10; house wine £9.
Payment all major credit cards. 10% service.
A Szechuan cuisine restaurant located in a converted church. Only Dublin Chinese with a Michelin entry. Children are treated as half price and the set lunch for £8 is tremendous value.
Babies/children catered for; child portions. Wheelchair friendly (except toilets). No smoking area (20). Booking advisable at weekends and for Sunday lunch. Air conditioned. Parties catered for. Takeaway. Ground floor. Stairs.

Welcome Chinese Restaurant
18 Maypark, Malahide Road, Donnycarney, Dublin 5
Tel 327222/327110
Seating 60
Open 5pm-1pm seven days.
Average £13.50.
Payment all major credit cards; EC, TC.
10% service.
Babies/children allowed before 8pm. Wheelchair friendly (except toilets). No smoking area (12). Booking advisable. Takeaway and free delivery within 3 miles. Ground floor access.

The Orchid Szechuan
120 Pembroke Road, Ballsbridge, Dublin 4
Tel 6600629
Seating 60
Open 12.30pm-2.15pm Mon-Fri, 6.30pm-midnight Mon-Sat; closed Sun.
Average £16 (dinner); house wine £10.20.
Payment all major credit cards; EC, TC.
10% service.
Babies/children allowed until 7pm. Not wheelchair friendly. No smoking area (5). Booking advisable. Private parties catered for. Takeaway. Ground floor.

TAKEAWAYS

Fu Moon Chinese Takeaway
St. Bridgets, Newtownpark Avenue, Blackrock, Co Dublin
Tel 2883057
Open 5pm-12.30pm Sun-Thurs; 5pm-1am Fri-Sat.
Average from £7.50
The spare ribs are 'yummy'. Delivery in the local area 6pm-11pm.

The Bamboo Home Delivery
Ranelagh, Dublin 6
Tel 962995
Open 6pm-11pm seven days
Average from £6
Speciality: king prawns and green pepper with black bean sauce. Vegetarian available. Delivery within a two mile radius 60p.

China Cottage
Unit 4 31/33 The Triangle, Ranelagh, Dublin 6
Tel 963533
Open 5pm-12.30am Mon-Thurs; 5pm-1am Fri-Sat; 5.30pm-midnight Sun.
Average from £8

Mr Tang Takeaway
133 Lower Rathmines Road, Dublin 6
Tel 966613
Open 5pm-1am Mon-Thurs; 5pm-1.30am Fri-Sat; 5pm-12.30am Sun.
Average £8.75
Speciality fried chicken with green pepper and black bean sauce. Vegetarian available.

Treasures Takeaway
2 The Hill, Stillorgan, Co Dublin.
Tel 2836066
Open 5pm-12.30am Mon-Thurs; 5pm-1am Fri/Sat; 5.30pm-midnight Sun; Thurs/Fri 12.30pm-2pm.
Speciality: mixed combination dishes.

Jumbo Takeaway
72 St Laurence's Park, Stillorgan, Co Dublin
Tel 2882374
Open noon-2pm, 5.15pm-12.30am Mon-Thurs; noon-2pm, 5.15pm-1am Fri/Sat; 5.15pm-12.30am Sun.
Average £6
Delivery 6pm-10.45pm.

Kambo Chinese Takeaway
21 Church Road, Ballybrack, Co Dublin
Tel 2824397
Open 5.30pm-12.30am seven days
Average £6
Speciality beef with spring onions, Szechuan mixed. Vegetarian available.
Parties catered for. Delivery.

Chess Chinese Takeaway
Unit 12 The Park, Prussia Street, Dublin 7
Tel 383694
Open 5pm-1am seven days
Average £6.50
Speciality: Peking and Szechuan cuisine. Vegetarian available.
Wheelchair friendly (except toilets). Delivery charge 70p.

Ayumi-Ya Restaurant
Newpark Centre, Newtownpark Avenue, Blackrock, Co Dublin
Tel 2831767
Seating 60
Open 7pm-11pm Mon-Sat; 6pm-10pm Sun
Average £15; £14.95 set meal; house wine £9.50. Fully licensed.
Payment all major credit cards; EC, TC.
10% service.
This restaurant has two sections - one conventional western, the other with low chairs which should be sat on in crossed leg fashion. The latter is much more fun. Entertainment is provided by taped Japanese music. If sushi - thin slices of raw fish wrapped with seaweed - is not to your taste, there are many alternatives. Try yakitori or tempura as starters and teriyaki as a main course or if this is your first time, order the omakase menu, a type of tasting menu at the discretion of the chef. Vegetarian available.
Babies/children catered for, child portions and menu. No smoking area (20). Booking essential at weekends. Private room for parties. Takeaway by arrangement. Smart casual dress. Ground floor. Stairs to toilets.

Ayumi-Ya Japanese Steakhouse
Basment, 132 Lower Baggot Street, Dublin 2.
Tel 6620233
Seating 40
Open 12.30pm-2.30pm; 6pm-11.30pm Mon-Thurs;12.30pm-2.30pm, 6pm-12.30am Fri; 6pm-12.30am Sat.
Average £10; £6.95 lunch; house wine £9.50
Payment all major credit cards; EC, TC, LV.
10% service at lunchtime
Japanese steakhouse offering a more limited menu than its parent restaurant. Specialities are kushi-age (deep fried food on skewers), teriyaki. Vegetarian available.
Babies/children catered for, child portions and menu. Not wheelchair friendly. No smoking area (15). Takeaway. Smart casual dress. Stairs down.

Rasa Sayang Oriental Restaurant
16 Merrion Road, Ballsbridge, Dublin 4
Tel 6608833/6608358
Seating 54
Open 2.30pm-2.30pm Mon-Fri; 6pm-midnight Mon-Thurs; 6pm-1am Fri/Sat
Average £6.50 lunch; £17.50 dinner; house wine £8.90, glass £2.30
Payment AmEx, DC; EC, TC. 10% service for dinner.
"Rasa Sayang", (Malaysian for "Feelings of Love"), is a small restaurant, whose open fire and predominantly rose-pink hue contribute to making a relaxed atmosphere. With a Malaysian name, we felt we should sample the satay - Malaysian satay, not to be comfused with the Chinese variety, comes with a spicy peanut sauce which was a little hotter than usual, but nonetheless quite delicious. The service is cheerful and pleasant, which makes a change from some establishments.
Babies/children catered for, child portions; high

chairs. Not wheelchair friendly. No smoking area (12). Booking advisable. Private room for parties. Takeaway by arrangement. Neat casual dress. Stairs.

Langkawi
46 Upper Baggot Street, Dublin 4
Tel 6687760
Seating 50
Open 12.30pm-2.30pm Mon-Fri; 6pm- midnight seven days
Average £15; £18 five-course set dinner; £8.95 four course lunch and early bird; house wine £8.75.
Payment all major credit cards. 10% service.
Langkawi, to the uninitiated, is an unspoilt island of Malaysia; also, the marriage seat of Linda and Alex Hosey who decided, upon settling in Ireland, to title their restaurant accordingly. That was over two years ago and this almost missable exterior on Baggot Street has become a quietly popular, if most unpublicised venue, for lovers of fiery oriental cuisine. So much so that they've been featured in Malaysian Airways in-flight magazine. The food is interesting with Alex concocting his own Thai pickles and condiments. Lunch (£8.95 - almost a sell-out for four courses), is an ideal introduction and the chef will kindly lower the tone for those not wishing for scorchmarks in their mouths.
Babies/children catered for early evening; child portions. Not wheelchair friendly. Booking advisable. Takeaway by arrangement. Ground floor.

Salty Dog Restaurant
3a Haddington Terrace, Dun Laoghaire, Co Dublin
Tel 2808015
Seating 40
Open 7pm-11pm Tues-Sat; 5pm-11pm Sun; closed Mon.
Average £13.50 including coffee; £13.50 set meals; house wine £9.50.
Payment all major credit cards; EC, TC. 10% service.
Haddington Terrace, tucked away off Adelaide Road and overlooking the ferry terminal is well worth finding in order to sample Rijst Tafel, literally 'rice table', which is the speciality of this restaurant. A curious mix of Victorian Irish (leather topped tables) a selection of items from Indonesia and the Middle East and Persian prayer mats on the walls all combine to create a cosy, intimate ambience. .
Babies/children catered for Sunday. No smoking area (10). Booking advisable weekends. Private parties up to 30 catered for. Basement. Stairs.

Mr Hung's Sawadee Restaurant
3 Lower Kilmacud Road, Stillorgan, Co Dublin
Tel 2888727
Seating 110
Open noon-2.30, 6pm-12.30am Mon-Fri; 6pm-12.30am Sat/Sun
Average £20; £16-18 table d'hôte dinner; house wine £9.90. Fully licensed
Payment all major credit cards; EC, TC. 10% service.
Babies/children catered for; high chairs. No smoking area (20). Booking advisable. Private room for parties. Takeaway. Neat casual dress. Ground floor. Stairs.

Jules Restaurant
3a The Crescent, Monkstown, Co Dublin
Tel 2843023
Seating 120
Open noon -2.30pm, 7pm-11pm Mon-Sat; 12.30pm-3.30pm lunch Sunday.
Average £16; £12.95 Sunday buffet; house wine £9.95. Fully licensed.
Payment all major credit cards. 10% service.
A combination of European, Thai and Chinese cuisine. Chef has Toque D'Or certificate. Interesting two tiered restaurant with lots of plants and a fish pond. Entertainment is provided by a piano on weekdays and at weekends, a belly dancer.
Babies/children catered for; high chairs and baby changing room, nappies supplied.

Chili Club

1 Anne's Lane, (off South Anne Street), Dublin 2
Tel 6773721
Seating 42
Open12.30pm-2.30pm Mon-Fri; 7pm-11pm Mon-Sat; closed Sun
Average £13-14. £10 set lunch; house wine £9.
Payment all major credit cards; EC, TC.
Service of eight or more

Small, cosy and atmospheric. Secluded entry location with forbidding crossed swords etched on a black door with large brass knocker defy you to 'Knock, if you dare!' The narrow hallway makes believe you're intruding in somebody's house. Tables inside are happily well-spaced and allow for privacy in a small low-ceilinged room with a standard gas-coalfire in the hearth. The food is authentic, superb and reasonably priced; seasonal chillies make the eyelids glow while the bar upstairs, with closely knit tables, is ideal for carousing larger parties. Vegetarian available.

Babies/children allowed during the day. Not wheelchair friendly. No smoking area (12 upstairs). Booking essential. Private room for parties up to 16. Takeaway by arrangement Ground floor. First floor and stairs up.

Exotic

The mixed bag of exotic Dublin eateries has tended to be an ephemeral one. Often the brainchild of homesick ex-pats or returned travellers, these minority restaurants tended to start up on a shoestring in low-rent districts, only to quietly pack their camel saddle bags when commercial realities set in.

The Tree of Idleness along Bray seafront is the exceptional senior citizen of them all. Founded by the talented Akis Courtelles who contrived to present authentic Greek Cypriot food with European refinement, the tradition is maintained and looks set to continue as a landmark.

Various middle eastern cuisines are making tentative inroads to Dublin eating-out habits, putting mainstays like chickpeas, pitta bread and tabbouleh into common coinage even on mainstream menus. After several false starts, TexMex has been given a great boost of late by the availability of Mexican and American beers which successfully partner South of the Border tapas, chilli and beans. Most recent flurry of activity has been in the Cajun/creole area - worth watching to see if there is true grit in hominy grits and blackened fish.

Poco Loco
32 Parliament Street, Dublin 2
Tel 6791950
Seating 55
Open noon-midnight Mon-Fri; 5pm-midnight Sat; 6pm-11pm Sun Mar 17-Christmas.
Average £8.50; £3.75 starter/main course lunch; house wine litre £8.95. Fully licensed.
Payment A, V; EC, TC, LV.
Lively Mexican restaurant where everything spells colour - the walls are solid colours varying in boldness and hue from one to the next; the food is a mash of brown, red, white, green and orange - a melange any self-respecting obscure African nation's flag would be proud of; the tabletops and, of course, the staff. Cheap and hugely cheerful, a favourite of young Temple Bar denizens. The recent addition of a bar allows diners to cool jalapeno burns on imported beers. Prices are reasonable, service speedy, desserts awe-inspiring and the venue not one to take your bank manager for that overdraft extension request - especially weekends.
Babies/children tolerated. Wheelchair friendly (except toilets). No smoking area (4). Booking advisable for eight or more. Takeaway by arrangement. Ground floor. Stairs to toilets.

The Tree of Idleness
Seafront, Bray, Co Wicklow
Tel 2863498
Seating 55
Open 7.30pm-11pm Tues-Sat; 7.30pm-10pm Sun; closed Mon
Average £22-25; £15-19 set price midweek; house wine choice of three £10
Payment all major credit cards; EC,TC.
10% service.
The only Bray restaurant featured in **Edibilia.** We drew a line at Dun Laoghaire, making this one exception. Now 14 years old (an exception in itself), this Greek/Cypriot venue suffered the loss of its owner-chef in 1992 but nonetheless continues to impact with imaginative, well-rehearsed ethnic dishes and a good seafood selection. One of the most extensive wine lists in the British Isles and measured, unobtrusive service make the Tree of Idleness a real out-of-town treat. Pride of place is reserved for the dessert trolley which is home to about 25 options with a heavy emphasis on exotic fruits.
Babies/children allowed early. No smoking area (8). Booking advisable. Private room for parties. Ground floor.

Eureka Restaurant
(above Baggot Inn)
142 Lower Baggot Street, Dublin 2
Tel 6762868
Seating 60
Open 12.30pm-2.30pm Mon-Fri; 6pm-12.30am seven days

Average £13; £5 lunch; house wine £8.95. Fully licensed.
Payment A, V; EC, TC. 10% service.
White walls, Greek memorabilia and taped Greek music set the scene, at a pinch reminiscent of Mykonos and past holidays. Starters range from grilled sardines to feta tighaniti to Greek salad. The mezzes - a selection of small portions allows the diner to run the gamut of Greek cuisine without paying a fortune. Well worth visiting. Bring along your copy of **Edibilia** and you will be given a complimentary ouzo! Vegetarian available.
Babies/children under 12 catered for till 9pm, child portions. Not wheelchair friendly. Booking advisable. Private room for parties. Takeaway by arrangement. Stairs.

Break for the Border
Johnson Place, Dublin 2
Tel 4780300
Seating 150
Open 12.30pm-2.30pm, 11pm-2am Mon-Fri; 5pm-11pm Sun-Thurs; nightclub 11.30pm-2am Wed-Sat.
Average £12; £4.75 lunch; house wine £9.65. Fully licensed.
Payment all major credit cards; EC, TC.
This Tex Mex restaurant which opened at the end of 1992, features the 3Ds - drinking, dining and dancing! With authentic Mexican memorabilia and timber floor, it really comes to life after 9 with the arrival of the DJ when a nightclub atmosphere sets in - the nightclub proper operates at weekends - and dancing starts. Specialities are margheritas and fajitas. Vegetarian available.
Babies/children catered for, child portions; high chairs. No smoking area (35). Bookings Mon-Thurs only. Takeaway by arrangement. Ground floor. Stairs and lift.

Ali Baba Restaurant
87/88 South Great Georges Street, Dublin 2
Tel 6778796
Seating 70
Open 12.50pm-3.30pm, 5.30pm-11.30pm seven days
Average £10; £10.95 four course set meals; house wine £7.95.

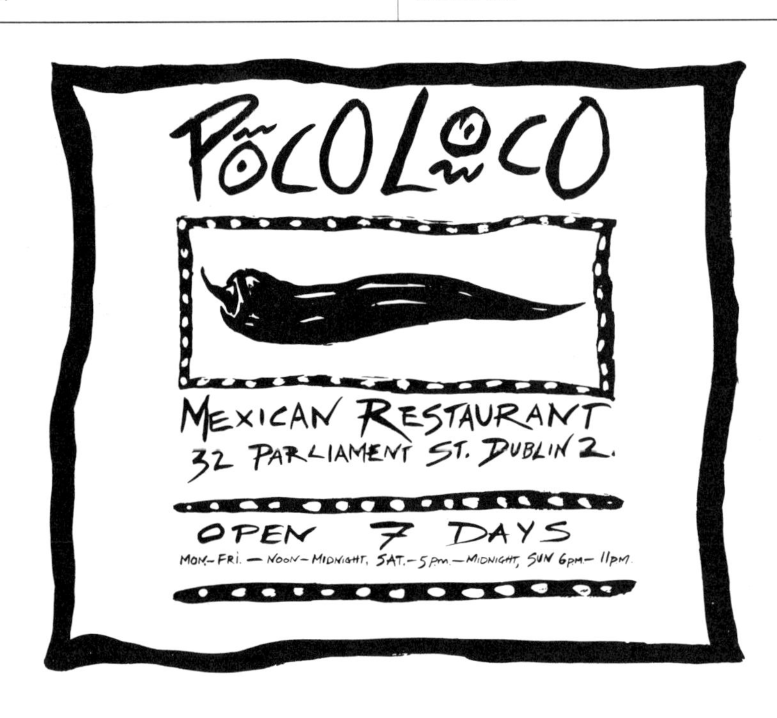

Payment all major credit cards, EC, TC.
Arabian restaurant features exotic dishes like hummus, tahini and falafel or mezzes. Main dishes include charcoal grilled chicken with onion, black peppers and herbs all charcoal grilled or the fish of the day cooked in spicy thick tomato sauce served on a bed of rice, complete with a side salad. There is easy listening live music every night, either a guitarist or a key board player. This is a late night restaurant, come after everything else is closed. Speciality is fish hot pot. Vegetarian available.
Babies/ children catered for, child portions and menu during the day; high chairs and baby changing room. Wheelchair friendly (except toilets). No smoking area (12) Booking advisable. Takeaway. Ground floor. Stairs.

Omar Khayyam
51 Wellington Quay, Dublin 2
Tel 6775758
Seating 45
Open noon-4pm, 6pm-midnight seven days
Average £15; £7.50 lunch; house wine £9.
Payment all major credit cards; EC, TC, LV
The only Egyptian restaurant in Dublin. Both decor and music are in keeping with this claim and the only thing lacking is an Egyptian wine, although there is one from the Lebanon. For those unfamiliar with this cuisine, Arabian mezze, including hummus, feta cheese, stuffed vine leaves, chicken wings, would be an ideal introduction, followed by a mixed grill of assorted kebabs again served with tahini. There is also baclava - the honey and pistachio pastry available in every cafe east of Suez and west of Muscat, and Arabic coffee to end. A belly dancer provides weekend entertainment. Vegetarian available.
Babies/children catered for, child portions. No smoking area (15). Booking advisable weekends. Takeaway.

Baton Rouge Restaurant
119 St. Stephen's Green, Dublin 2
Tel 4751181
Seating 80
Open 6pm-12.30am seven days; noon - 3pm brunch, 6pm-12.30am Sun
Average £15; house wine £9. Fully licensed.
Payment all major credit cards; EC, TC, LV.
Service charge for eight or more.
In the last 18 months, this address has sounded the death knell for The Green Room and Whites on the Green, so will it be third time lucky for enterprising anchorman, Robbie Fox, who takes over the steering with Baton Rouge, a lush deep-south creole cornucopia? The basement lounge area has its own private bar with a bordello feel to it (not Lillie's) while upstairs is woodier and roomier with a central mezzanine. Best value of all here is the Sunday jazz brunch - on offer is a choice of eight entrees (eggs Benedict, fillet pork piquant, panéed veal with fettucine), complete with appetiser and tea/coffee for anything from £4.50-7.25! Your dining pleasure will be enhanced by the mellow playing of a jazz ensemble who will look remarkably bored as you gabble collective about Saturday Night/Sunday Morning. Whatever you do, don't skimp on the Popcorn à la Baton Rouge (£1 extra) - they're a sucker's dream!

Babies/children catered for, child portions. No smoking (16). Booking advisable. Casual elegant dress. Ground floor.

Judge Roy Beans
45 Nassau Street, Dublin 2
Tel 6797539
Seating 100
Open noon-midnight seven days
Average £11.50; £4.25 lunch special soup, main course, coffee/tea; £5.50 minimum after 5pm; house wine £9. Fully licensed.
Payment all major credit cards; LV
Judge Roy's is a restaurant and bar with a young-at-heart demeanour. TexMex is what they're after - nachos, chilli, bar-b-q burgers, tacos, enchiladas, fajitas - all begging to be washed down with a thirst-slaking foreign beer. With the bar on hand and revvin' to go, it's a neat concept. Prices aren't overcooked, decor unelaborate and the venue is very popular, especially at weekends when no bookings are accepted over the 'phone.
Babies/children allowed. Not wheelchair friendly. No smoking area (20). Booking essential weekdays. Private room for parties. Takeaway rolls, ba snacks. Ground floor.

Cedar Tree
11A St Andrew's Street, Dublin 2
Tel 6772121
Seating 50
Open 5.30pm-11.30pm seven days; -10.45pm Sun
Average £20; £16 mezze; house wine £9.95.
Payment all major credit cards; EC, TC.
12 ½% service
Located in Dublin's most densely populate restaurant street, the Cedar Tree has receive praise from many quarters since its establish ment more than seven years ago. For a quin tessentially Lebanese restaurant, the staff ar quntessentially Dublinese but very able Based in the bowels of 11A St Andrew' Street, it feels like a cavern where many alter native rockers scoop and sup into the we hours. Mezzes are a main feature of the menu with three selections-for-two checking in a £22, £48 and £30 (vegetarian) and featurin hummus, tabbouleh, vine leaves, chilli kafta chicken mussahab to name but a few. A goo rangy introduction if you're not familiar wit this ethnic variety.
Babies/children allowed up to 7pm; high chairs Not wheelchair friendly. No smoking area (6) Booking advisable. Smart casual dress. Takeawa by arrangement. Stairs.

The Levant
11B St. Andrew's Street, Dublin 2
Tel 6772121
Seating 54 restaurant/16 mezze
Open noon-3pm Mon-Fri; 6pm-midnight seven days; 6pm-midnight mezze bar seven days
Average £14.00 dinner; £ 14.50 five-course set dinner; £8.95 four-course lunch; house wine £9.50. Fully licensed.
Payment A, V; EC.
Mediterranean restaurant with open kitchen The mezze bar is carpeted while the restaurant has high ceilings and a dark wood floor Copper ornaments, rugs and vases add to the ambience. Vegetarian available.

Babies/children catered for, child portions up to 7pm; high chairs. Not wheelchair friendly. Booking advisable. Ground floor. Stairs up to toilets. Takeaway by arrangement.

Little Lisbon
2 Upper Fownes Street, Dublin 2
Tel 6711274
Seating 80
Open noon-11pm Sun-Thurs; noon-1am Fri/Sat
Average £9.95; house wine £9.95.
Payment all major credit cards; EC, TC, LV.
10% service.
A busy little restaurant in the Temple Bar district, Little Lisbon, with white-washed walls, is reminiscent of the Algarve. Diners can bring their own wine with no corkage charge. The menu features typical Portuguese fare. Grilled sardines evoke marvellous memories of summer holidays. Snails in garlic sauce are served Spanish style on a bed of salt! There is also a Portuguese paella and mussels in port and portions are generous. Specialities are seafood and game. Vegetarian available.
Babies/children allowed; baby changing room. Wheelchair friendly (except toilets). No smoking area (15). Booking advisable weekends. Private room for parties. Ground floor. Stairs.

Valparaiso Restaurant
99 Monkstown Road, Monkstown, Co Dublin
Tel 2801992
Seating 55
Open 6.30pm-11.30pm Mon-Sat; 6pm-10pm Sun
Average £15; £10.95 tapas; house wine £9.50.
Payment all major credit cards; EC, TC.
10% for six or more.
Restaurant situated over Goggins pub behind a bright blue door. White-washed walls decorated with woven rugs and bright blue shutters give a real Mediterranean holiday feel. Flavours are strong - lashings of garlic with everything - and portions generous. Tapas, paella, stuffed chicken, fillet of beef with sauce, Catalan potatoes (slightly spicy sautéd chunks and very good). Desserts include brown bread ice-cream with hot chocolate sauce.

Babies/children catered for, child portions. Not wheelchair friendly. No smoking area (10). Booking advisable. Takeaway by arrangement. Stairs.

La Paloma
17B Temple Bar (Asdill's Row), Dublin 2
Tel 6777392
Open noon-12.30 seven days.
Average £15; £7.50 minimum after 6pm; £16 table d'hôte; house wine £10. Fully licensed.
Payment A, V; EC, TC.
10% service for eight or more.
Spanish restaurant and bar; one of the few but growing number in Ireland specialising in Spanish food like tapas. The house speciality, paella, should serve two but would easily do three. The limited dessert menu includes a delicious mud pie with butterscotch sauce. A jazz band on Sunday, Spanish guitarist and Flamenco dancer are on hand to provide entertainment. Vegetarian available.
Babies/children catered for, child menu; high chairs. No smoking area (10). Ground floor.

Tante Zoe
1 Crow Street, Dublin 2
Tel 6794407
Seating100
Open noon-6pm, 6pm-midnight seven days; closed Sun
Average £15; £5.75 minimum 6pm-midnight; £9 three course lunch + tea/coffee; house wine £8.75
Payment all major credit cards; EC, TC, LV.
10% service for eight or more.
Dublin's original Cajun/creole restaurant specialising in jambalaya and blackened fish. This cuisine which originated in Louisiana, is a combination of African, French and Spanish, once believed to be a mixture of the food of the poor negros who lived along the waterways and swamps of Louisiana and the more aristocratic cuisine of the up tempo New Orleans city folk. This fashionable restaurant, with its cool music and tucked away on the outer reaches of Temple Bar, is for the young-at-heart. Real alligator features prominently on the menu along with Alabama rissoles (seasoned meatballs served

fondue style with a spicy cheese) delicious but difficult to eat elegantly and Cajun popcorn (huge prawns in seasoned batter served with a pepper flake sauce for dipping). Desserts are truly American with outrageous names like Fat Man's Misery and Mississippi Mud Slide. It's a fun place with a difference.
Babies/children allowed at lunch time only. Not wheelchair friendly. No smoking area (8). Booking advisable, essential at weekend. Private room for parties. Ground floor. Stairs.

The Cactus Moon
George's Avenue, Blackrock, Co Dublin
Tel 2882048
Seating 100 upstairs
Open noon-11pm seven days
Average £14; house wine £8.50.
Payment A, V; EC
Opened in May this year, this restaurant with a very strong Cajun theme aims to provide more than just food. Downstairs in the spacious reception area is a large bar with stools while upstairs is open plan and sparsely decorated to look like a farrier's with saddles and horseshoes on the walls. There is a strong emphasis on entertainment with both country and western and Cajun music. Specialities include Cactus prawn special, Cajun fish special and red rooster Baton Rouge.
Babies/children catered for; high chairs available. Not wheelchair friendly. No smoking area. Booking advisable. Takeaway.

Taverna Greek Restaurant
33 Wicklow Street, Dublin 2
Tel 6773665
Seating 80
Open noon-2.30pm, 5pm-midnight Sun-Thurs; -1am Fri/Sat
Average £12.95; £4.95 set two courses + coffee; house wine £9.50
Payment A, AmEx, V; EC, TC.
10% service evenings.
Established seven years, this restaurant is situated in the heart of Dublin. Specialities are mezzes and kebabs. Vegetarian 50% available
Babies/children catered for, child portions. Not wheelchair friendly. Booking advisable. Private

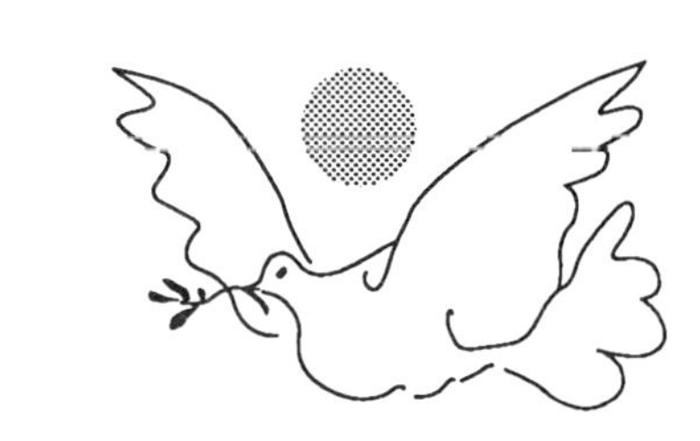

parties catered for. Ground floor. Stairs down to toilets.

Señor Sassi's
146 Upper Leeson Street, Dublin 4
Tel 6684544
Seating 65
Open noon-2.30 Mon-Fri; 6pm-midnight Mon-Sat; 5.30pm-10.30pm Sun.
Average £16-18; £7.95 or £9.50 set lunch; Italian house wine £9.50
Payment all major credit cards; EC, TC.
10% service for six or more.
Contemporary and casual are two words best describing Senor Sassi's. Located next door to the similarly vibrant Cafe Java, only a spit from the Burlington, the restaurant has a real Mediterranean feel about it, augmented if the weather is fine, particularly true of the extended conservatory. The menu is a confluence of Moroccan, Spanish, Italian, fowl, steaks and vegetarian on average about 15% more expensive than the Italian (Da Vicenzo) around the corner. Especial note should be made of the sassy olive bread. specials menu.
Babies/children catered for, child portions up to 8.30pm. No smoking area (10). Booking advisable. Private room for parties. Ground floor. Stairs.

Al's Restaurant
South William Street, Dublin 2
Tel 6791517
Seating 50
Open noon- midnight Mon-Sat; closed Sun
Average £12; £7.95 lunch; £10.95 pre-theatre 10.95; house wine £9.50. Fully licensed.
Payment A, V; EC, TC.
Al's has the atmosphere of a cellar with scrubbed floorboards, stripped pine chairs and an interesting clutter of pictures and musical instruments on the walls. The accent is on good food at a good price. Entertainment consists of live music and diners are invited to participate. A popular starter is the combination platter - a mini-mezze served around a mound of hummus as it is supposed to be eaten with olive oil and garlic and washed down with pints of cold Guinness. It really is a party restaurant. 10/10 for enjoyment, 7/10 for food.
Speciality is lamb Dijon, Robespierre (steak cooked in mustard and olive oil). Vegetarian available.
Babies/children catered for, child portions; high chairs. Not wheelchair friendly. No smoking area (6). Booking essential. Takeaway by arrangement. Ground floor. Stairs.

Wholefood

A few years ago, if you wanted a vegetarian meal in Dublin, you ordered the main course minus the meat but oh, how things have changed! If you're a vegetarian, vegan, enjoy wholefood or organic foods, or even have special dietary needs, you can now dine out in style in many of the excellent venues around the city. Many non-specialist restaurants now include vegetarian options but several places are dedicated exclusively to the vegetarian/wholefood palate.

Most are located within five minutes' walking distance of Grafton Street, all offering excellent value with large portions and a wide choice of dishes. Try Cornucopia on Wicklow Street whose colour-coded menu indicates whether dishes are gluten-free, wheat-free or dairy-free. It is also open up to 9pm and is frequented by an interesting crowd. Blazing Salads at the top of the Powerscourt Townhouse, with tables located on the airy top floor of this elegant shopping development, also tags a mainly macrobiotic menu so those on a special diet can eat with an easy mind. You'll be amazed at the range of mouth-watering main courses, salads, soups and desserts. Sadly, it is not open at night but it's worth noting that it offers a takeaway service. Dublin is a good place to start if you want to be introduced to vegetarian/wholefood dishes.

There are a number of demi-vegetarian restaurants too so there's no need to segregate your friends when meeting for a meal! The Coffee Bean on Nassau Street or The Cellary in Temple Bar both offer nutritious food with a real home-cooked flavour.

Whichever one you select, you can be sure of good value, a convivial atmosphere and a real choice. Even if you're not a vegetarian, they're well worth a visit - you could end up being converted!

The Coffee Bean
4 Nassau Street, Dublin 2
Tel 6797140
Seating 80
Open 10.30am-3.30pm Mon-Fri
Average £6.50; £1.80 minimum 12.30pm-2.30pm; house wine £7.95, ¼ bottle £1.95; glass £1.60.
Payment LV

There is a certain insouciance about The Coffee Bean. Tucked away on the first and second floors of a Nassau Street building, signalled only by a sandwich-board overgrown by next door's vegetable stalls, they don't seem to want to be found and they rarely, if ever, advertise. The counter service is far from thrifty, the upward stairs are narrow and the queue frequently too long. Yet, if you are prepared, the food is plentiful and excellent; window seats on a sunny day offer the most pleasant view (Trinity playing fields) in central Dublin - no extra charge; and prices are remarkably reasonable. Just another corker in a well-represented sector.

Babies/children catered for, child portions. Not wheelchair friendly. No smoking area (30). Stairs.

Cornucopia
19 Wicklow Street, Dublin 2
Tel 6777583
Seating 44
Open 8am-8pm Mon-Wed/Fri; 8am-9pm Thurs; 8am-6pm Sat; closed Sun.
Average £5; £1.50 minimum 12.30pm-2pm.

The thing about most city centre restaurants is that you can predict a mad rush at lunchtime with troughs of activity either side. The thing about Cornucopia is that you can't. It is as likely to be thronged at 12 noon as it is at 4pm as it is at lunch and with good reason - the portions befit the title. When filling the questionnaire for **Edibilia,** the 'Average' section (i e price of three courses) suddenly appeared de trop as a lady earwigging the conversation jabbed in with "But you'll never finish three courses here." If you love burgers and chocolate malts, avoid Cornucopia. If you feel guilty at too much healthy aubergine bake and red bean and spinach strudel with

lashings of imaginative "two salads 10p extra" salads and turfs of lumpy, seedy, brown bread, just pack a Mars bar for afters. Winner of Walkers Award for Best Vegetarian Restaurant.
Babies/children catered for, child portions. Not wheelchair friendly. No smoking area (32). Takeaway. Ground floor. Stairs down to toilets.

Wellfed Cafe
6 Crow Street, Dublin 2
Tel 6772234
Seating 80
Open 12.30pm-8.30pm Mon-Sat; closed Sun.
Average £4.70; occasional specials.
Restaurant that is part of a well established co-op offering a wide and varied entirely vegetarian menu at affordable prices. Winner of Walkers Vegetarian Dublin Award for Excellence in Cuisine. There is a choice of 4/5 main courses which are served with a selection of bean and green salads - in full or half portions; a different soup each day is served with brown bread or scone. The vegetarian burger is, in my view, the best available and is served with either a tomato or cheese sauce. This is good food freshly prepared before your eyes, in a friendly atmosphere where vegetarians are not an afterthought but the main focus of attention!
Babies/children catered for, child portions on request; high chairs and baby changing room. Wheelchair friendly (except toilets). No smoking area (40). Booking advisable. Restaurant available for private parties after 8.30pm .

Blazing Salads
Powerscourt Townhouse, Dublin 2
Tel 6719552
Seating 80
Open 10am-6pm Mon-Sat; closed Sun.
Average £6.25; £1.50 minimum 12.30pm-2pm; £4.25 set price with main course; house wine (Australian Chardonnay only) £7.40, glass £1.50
The type and location of this restaurant are complementary. Health and fitness are what you'll need to scale the heights to the second floor of the Powerscourt Centre and both these ingredients appear on the menu in very thin disguise ... even the drinks are good for you - pressed juices, multi-vitamin drinks and cassis (£1.20) - honey blended with yoghurt and fruit of your choice - all bellow their goodness at you from the chalk board. Staff are friendly and helpful and main courses include vegetarian pizzas and lasagnes. Soups start at £1 and ice-creams (yes, you're allowed!) are homemade. An all-wood restaurant, a thoroughfare for browsers and a good selection of teas and coffees.
Babies/children catered for, child portions; high chairs. Not wheelchair friendly. No smoking area (26). Booking advisable. Takeaway.

Food For Thought
56 Lower Georges Street, Dun Laoghaire, Co Dublin
Tel 2841035
Seating 40
Open 10am-3pm
Average £1-5; wine ¼ bottle £1.85
Payment LV.
Cheerful ambience set off by pictures by local artists. Home-cooked fresh food on premises; morning teas, coffees, lunches, luscious cakes. Speciality is home-made soup.
Babies/children catered for, ½ portions. Not wheelchair friendly. No smoking area (14). Takeaway. Stairs.

101, Talbot
Upstairs, 100-102 Talbot Street, Dublin 1
Tel 8745011
Seating 80
Open:10am-11pm Mon-Sat; closed Sun
Average £12.65; £2.75 lunch minimum; £7.75 set lunch; house wine £7.95. Fully licensed.
Payment all major credit cards; EC, TC, LV
Situated close to the Abbey theatre, this light airy restaurant is ideal for pre- or post-theatre dining and is also a favourite with theatre-people. 101 Talbot is as unprepossessing as it is a real find. Located amidst the Poundstretchers and streetlighter and tobacco urchins of Talbot Street and just

around the corner from theatreland, this is a sanctuary of taste in a seedy underworld. This is a wholefood restaurant that caters for carnivores - or the other way round, depending on your side of the fence. Service is unobtrusive, prices competitive, the air convivial and the food international and delicious.
Babies/children catered for, child portions; high chairs and baby changing facilities. Not wheelchair friendly. No smoking area (30). Booking essential. Stairs.

Cellary Restaurant
1 Lower Fownes Street, Temple Bar, Dublin 2
Tel 6710362
Seating 40
Open 9am-11.30pm Mon-Sat; 9am-9pm Mon/Tues (winter).
Average £12.50 three-course à la carte dinner; house wine (Italian) £9.50; also allowed to bring your own.
Payment EC, TC.
This small demi-vegetarian (serves white meat and fish) restaurant in the heart of Temple Bar is one of the Great Unexposeds. A little like some newspaper racing tipsters who deliberately tip their public the wrong horse to increase the odds on their real fancy, I am inclined to button my lip about the Cellary. However, I'm under obligation. It is small with black-painted tables and chairs and a small self-service counter that isn't strictly, as the staff might just rush your dish to your table when ready. Upstairs is stark with walls adorned with the finest of human beauty icons - so if your partner isn't up to scratch... The daytime menu changes when the house chef appears to replace the (almost) co-operative of friends. Food is well presented, of infinite freshness and the award for the best hummus in Dublin resides here (unofficially).
Babies/children catered for, child portions. Not wheelchair friendly. No smoking area (6). Booking advisable. Table outdoors. Private room for parties. Takeaway. Ground floor. Stairs.

Seafood

Long before Jonathan Swift was to record the price of Malahide herrings as six pence a dozen, and Dubliners fed oysters to their cats and salmon to their servants, wonderful fish, oysters, prawns and lobsters abounded in Irish waters.

Until more recently, knowing quite what to do with them in the kitchen was a different kettle of fish. While prawn cocktail and steak were de rigueur for the expense-account businessman, the late Ernie Evans in Kerry claimed to be the first restaurateur who made it all right for real men to eat fish. Butter drenched sole, garlic-scented mussels in wine and succulent salmon moved onto smart menus, never to be dislodged.

All of Dublin Bay is necklaced by gems of seafood specialists, from the King Sitric in Howth where Aidan McManus has glamorised some of the lesser known fish hauled off the boats in front of the restaurant, right around to Restaurant na Mara, Irish Rail's premier dining spot on the southernmost arm of the Bay. In town, the Periwinkle Seafood Bar twinkles as a landlocked beacon for aficionados of some of the city's freshest and least expensive seafood. Famous chowder, brown bread and crabmeat rolls attract daily queues to this spotless and unpretentious corner.

Turbot, sole and salmon, the king of fish, are the province of some of the grander restaurants, along with lobster and Dublin Bay prawns that no longer come from Dublin Bay. Visitors should note that sole known as Dover elsewhere is called black sole in Ireland and commands a premium price, often denoted by a discreet blank on the right hand side of the menu.

Restaurant na Mara
1 Harbour Road, Dun Laoghaire, Co Dublin
Tel 2806767
Seating 75
Open 12.30pm-2.30pm, 7pm-10.30pm Mon-Sat; closed Sun and bank holidays.
Average £25; £12.95 set lunch; £23 set dinner; house wine £9.50. Fully licensed.
Payment all major credit cards; EC, TC.
15% service charge.

When the Dublin-Kingstown (Dun Laoghaire) railway was inaugurated in 1834, the terminus was in Old Dun Laoghaire. However, a new terminus, designed by John Mulvany in the classical Victorian railway station-style, was built between 1844-1850 and became what is now Restaurant na Mara. Its location, beside the railway station and Sealink car ferry terminus and the seafront, makes it a popular venue for lovers of good seafood and local residents. The setting is stunning, befitting a restaurant which has the reputation of being

one of Dublin's finest, certainly in terms of seafood. The interior is best described as stylish with a warm pink hue predominating. Choose from the table d'hôte menu at £23 or expect to pay a bit more for à la carte. Rock oysters served warm with a smoked salmon and paloise sauce could be a good place to start but be sure there is an 'R' in the month! Follow with scallops bonne femme or for something a bit racier, try Dublin Bay prawns in garlic butter mornay. Flambées are always spectacular and add a fiery frisson to all dining occasions. The scallops can be flambéd in brandy or the prawns 'ignited' with orange curacao and lobster sauce. If the evening prices are a bit steep, lunch at this exciting restaurant at £12.75 is well worth it.
Babies/children catered for, child portions. No smoking area (25). Booking advisable. Private room for parties. Takeaway by arrangement. Neat casual dress. Ground floor.

The Guinea Pig Restaurant
17 Railway Road, Dalkey, Co Dublin.
Tel 2859055
Seating 50
Open 6pm-11pm seven nights; 12.30pm-3pm Sun
Average £25; £10.95 early bird 6pm-8pm and Sunday lunch; house wine £10.95.
Payment all major credit cards; EC, TC
People have been coming to this restaurant, which has a Victorian feel, since 1958, unique for Dublin. In 1986, owner Mervyn Stewart was crowned King of Dalkey in a ceremony with origins in the 1790s when a group of orators met in Dublin to discuss events of the day. The members who were also dedicated to a bit of fun, would elect from amongst themselves one who would hold the office of 'King' for a year. Dalkey has been nominated a heritage town so what better excuse than to go to Dalkey and enjoy a meal not only fit but prepared by a king!
Speciality is cold fresh prawns, grilled sole on the bone. Vegetarian on request.
Children and babies catered for, child portions; high chairs available. No smoking area (16). Booking advisible, essential at weekend. Private room for parties up to 30. Casual neat dress. Ground floor.

The Lobster Pot
9 Ballsbridge Terrace, Ballsbridge, Dublin 4
Tel 6680025/6609170
Seating 40
Open noon-2.30pm Mon-Fri; 6pm-10.30pm Mon-Sat; closed Sun
Average £22.50; house wine £ 9.50; corkage by arrangement. Fully licensed.
Payment all major credit cards; EC, TC.
12 ½% service
Situated beside RDS, Lansdowne Road and major hotels, this restaurant's clubby atmosphere is enhanced by subtle lighting, fresh flowers, polished copper and brass. Speciality is fresh fish. Vegetarian on request.
Not wheelchair friendly. No smoking area (8). Booking advisable. Smart dress. Stairs.

Perwinkle Seafood Bar
Powerscourt Townhouse, South William Street, Dublin 2.
Tel 6794203
Open 10.30am-5pm Mon-Sat; closed Sun
Average £6.50; house wine £7.25, glass £1.65.
Payment EC, TC, LV.
The Periwinkle is hidden in a corner of the Powerscourt Townhouse Centre, and for fish lovers it is well worth finding. Most of the seating is on high wooden stools at counter tops. In the middle of this is the self-service counter with a wide selection of hot dishes, salads and open sandwiches, for eating in or takeaway. Delicious and well renowned seafood chowder (£1.75) is served in either a mug or bowl. Salads are also offered in either a "plate" or "full" salad, priced from £4-£7/8 respectively, and include jumbo prawns, crab and fresh salmon. Daily, a hot food special is served with potatoes and vegetables or salads, again in two options according to size £4-£7. The great thing about this place is that there is a takeaway service because the Periwinkle, both because of its size and layout, gets very packed indeed.

Babies/children catered for, child portions; high chairs and baby changing room. No smoking area (30). Takeaway. Ground floor. Stairs.

King Sitric Fish Restaurant
East Pier, Howth, Co Dublin
Tel 325235
Seating 60
Open 6.30pm-11pm Mon-Sat; noon-3pm seafood & oyster bar Mon-Sat May-Sept only.
Average £25; £22 table d'hote 22; house wine £11.00. Fully licensed
Payment all major credit cards; EC, TC.
Named after King Sitric III, a Norse king of Dublin in the eleventh century who had a close association with Howth and was a son-in-law of Brian Boru, the famous Irish King. Situated on the harbour, close to the Howth yacht marina, where better to enjoy fresh fish? Enjoy an aperitif in the lounge which has magnificent views overlooking Balscadden Bay and in summer, watch the yacht racing. The menu contains a mouth-watering selection of mainly fish dishes prepared by chef/proprietor Aidan MacManus to many of his own original recipes and complemented by an excellent wine list. Speciality is fresh fish. Vegetarian available on request
Babies/children catered for, child portions; changing room facilities. No smoking area (30). Booking advisable. Private room for parties up to 40. Takeaway by arrangement. Informal neat dress. Ground floor. Stairs.

Kish Restaurant
Jurys Hotel, Ballsbridge, Dublin 4
Tel 6605000
Seating 48
Open 6.15pm-10.45pm Mon-Sat; closed Sun
Average £32.00; £25 five course set meal; house wine £10.50. Fully licensed.
Payment all major credit cards; EC, TC, LV.
12 ½% service.
Seafood restaurant. Entertainment - classical guitar four hours every evening and a baby grand piano. Named after the lighthouse and located in the upper shades of the Pavilion residents bar, this deceivingly high quality restaurant is a seafarer's delight for those able to afford it. With fish so fresh I could swear it moved and service like a cat to a wounded mouse, it takes some beating in the seafood stakes. However, you pay accordingly. The atmosphere may be upset or enhanced by the proximity of the Pavilion bar depending on your table. Specialities are seafood and shellfish. Vegetarian available.
No smoking area (12). Booking advisable. Neat dress. Ground floor.

Ante-Room Seafood Restaurant
20 Lower Baggot Street, Dublin 2
Tel 6618832
Seating 70
Open noon-3pm Mon-Fri; 6pm-10.30pm Mon-Sat; 6pm-9pm Sun
Average £18; £5.50 set lunch; £19.90 table d'hôte dinner; house wine £9.30. Fully licensed.
Payment all major credit cards; EC, TC, LV.
10% service evening.
This restaurant is part of the Georgian House Hotel complex which includes Maguire's pub, and, as its name implies, specialises in seafood. Within striking distance of most of the major hotels and close to Stephen's Green, it is also adjacent to the business heart of Dublin. Recommended are oysters and scallops in a white wine and cream sauce, served with piped potatoes. Speciality is platter of cold shellfish. Vegetarian on request.
Babies/children catered for, child portions; high chairs. Not wheelchair friendly. No smoking area (20). Booking advisable. Private room for parties. Neat casual dress. Stairs.

Lord Edward Seafood Restaurant
23 Christchurch Place, Dublin 8
Tel 542420
Seating 40
Open noon-10.45pm Mon-Fri; 6pm-10.45pm Sat
Average £20; £10.95 lunch; £20 table d'hote dinner; house wine £9.50. Fully licensed.
Payment all major credit cards; EC, TC.
This famous tavern, named after Lord Edward Fitzgerald, the fifth son of the Duke of Leinster, is situated in the oldest part of

Dublin. The fish restaurant, on the second floor above a traditional Irish pub, with leaded windows, high-backed chairs and bar tables, as well as a liberal smattering of antiques, has an olde worlde atmosphere and a window seat affords the diner a fine view of Christchurch. The table lunch is based on the price of the main course. Scallops and prawns Newburg are a speciality of the house and desserts include Bailey's chocolate cup. Vegetarian on request.
Babies/children catered for, child portions; baby changing room. Not wheelchair friendly. No smoking area (8). Booking advisable. Stairs.

Purty Kitchen
Old Dunleary Road, Dun Laoghaire, Co Dublin
Tel 2843576
Seating 80
Open 12.30pm-10pm seven days
Average £11; £15 dinner; French house wine £7.95. Fully licensed.
Payment A, V; TC.
Situated close to Dun Laoghaire harbour, this is a popular venue for a light tasty lunch. Everything is homemade and it has earned a reputation for its seafood chowder and homemade brown bread (£2.50). Open fresh seafood sandwiches are also served daily. Mouth-watering desserts include chocolate brandy biscuit cake. A typical old Irish pub with a floor over 80 years old with the pleasing decor that includes a traditional style bar. Cocktails on request. Entertainment is complimentary Irish traditional music in bar; blues rock five nights in Purty Loft music venue upstairs, one of the only live music venues southside which can accommodate up to 600.

Fox's Pub/Restaurant
Glencullen, Co Dublin
Tel 2955647
Seating 270
Open 10.30pm-midnight Mon-Sat; noon-11pm Sun.
Average £12 set-price meals for groups only; house wine £7.50. Fully licensed.
Payment all major credit cards; EC, TC.
Fox's, nestled high in the Dublin mountains at Glencullen, is a real trip from the city along spindly, bumpy narrow roads but adorned with the best of Irish countryside. Strange then that the place is very often full, and significantly, full of city-dwellers who have made the effort. The location is serene but when busy inside (live music seven nights) can be complete bedlam. Food is almost exclusively seafood, served informally but efficiently. The inside is a veritable maze of rooms and corners in dark surroundings with sawdust strewn flagstone floors and in winter, blazing hearths. (In Ireland, that applies to summer also!). Unusually Eichbaum beer available on draft - don't forget the drive home!
Babies/children allowed up to 7pm. Booking advisable, essential weekends. Tables outdoors. Private room for parties. Ground floor.

The Lighthouse Rooftop Restaurant
Dalkey Island Hotel, Coliemore Harbour, Dalkey, Co Dublin
Seating 45-50
Open 7pm-11pm Mon-Sat
Average £14.50-£23.50; set price for groups by arrangement; house wine £9.25, corkage £4.50
Payment all major credit cards. 10% service.
Idyllically located overlooking Dublin Bay, this restaurant specialises in fresh seafood and fillet steaks with options for vegetarians.
Babies/children catered for, child portions and menu; high chairs and baby changing room. No smoking area (10). Booking advisable. Private room for parties. Stairs.

Mullach Cottage Restaurant
4 Church Road, Malahide, Co Dublin
Tel 8451346
Seating 80
Open 8am-midnight seven days
Average £13.95 dinner; £5.95 three course lunch; £3.95 breakfast 8am-6pm; house wine £8.95
Payment all major credit cards; EC, TC, LV.
12 ½% service after 7pm
Dating back to 1972, this is Malahide's oldest restaurant with a cottage style dining area

on split levels. With breakfast served till 6pm, it is ideal for those who keep erratic hours. Specialising in seafood, lobster from £10 in season must make it one of the best buys in Ireland! Daily specials include black sole with a lobster sauce for £9.95. By and large, very good value.

Babies/children catered for, child portions and menu; high chairs and baby changing room. No smoking area (16). Booking advisable at night. Tables outdoors. Private room for parties. Ground floor. Stairs.

FOX'S PUB EST 1798

PURTY KITCHEN PURTY KITCHEN PURTY

Culture Vultures

Ireland is extremely rich in heritage and culture, a fact which has been one of the major tourist attractions for the country. The importance of the contribution it has made to Irish social life is reflected in the enhanced facilities now available in cultural venues, including 'eateries'.

The section takes a look at the 'edible offerings' located in cutural exhibition centres in Dublin. They range from large restaurants like Fitzers within the National Gallery, Merrion Square, to more unusual places like The Winding Stair Bookshop Cafe (av £3-£4) located near the Ha'penny Bridge. Two that should definitely not be missed are the recently opened Irish Film Centre in Temple Bar (excellent cappuccino coffee) and Chapter One in the Writers' Museum, Parnell Square (£12 pre-theatre three course dinner), a sister restaurant of The Old Dublin.

Several top quality restaurants have incorporated the cultural theme and are worth a visit for a special evening's entertainment. Take a look at The Lane Gallery on Pembroke Lane for lunch (av £7.50) or dinner (av £19 incl wine) where both sight and sound will be treated to an exhibition of contemporary Irish art (on sale) and serenaded by a resident pianist respectively.

Wherever the trail takes 'culture vultures', there are more than enough places to rest tired feet and enjoy a refreshing tea or coffee while soaking up the atmosphere of Dublin's best cultural offerings.

Chapter One

18/19 Parnell Square, Dublin 1
Tel 8782266/8732281
Seating 80
Open 12.30pm-2.30pm, 6pm-10.45pm Tues-Sun; closed Mon.
Average £22.50; £12 pre-theatre three course dinner; house wine (Chilean Sauvignon Blanc) £10.75. Fully licensed.
Payment all major credit cards; EC, TC.
10% service

The basement of the Writers' Museum is the location of this calm tastefully decorated restaurant. Casually arranged around its peach walls are paintings, sketches, sculpture and glass-work depicting characters in Ireland's rich literary heritage. The food complements the elegant surroundings and is, without exception, excellent. Irish goats' cheese, served on a marmalade coulis, was smooth in texture, the slight bite of the cheese nicely tempered by the coulis. Wild mushrooms in Grand Marnier were also delicious, the contrasting tastes clashing. As a main course, trout, cooked to perfection, was served with a curried tartare sauce which added a whole new taste to the fish. A delicious pastry roll filled with beans and vegetables would delight any vegetarian. Desserts included a black and white chocolate mousse, perfectly chocolatey, yet light, and a creamy cheesecake. Coffee and petits fours completed the experience. This is the place for a memorable meal in a relaxed atmosphere. Traditional music is played on Sunday.
Specialities include fish and seafood. Vegetarian available. Extensive wine list.
Babies/children catered for, child portions free; two high chairs. No smoking area (20). Booking Tables outdoors on roof garden. Selection of rooms for private parties. Basement. Stairs. Private car parking available.

Castle Vaults Bistro

Dublin Castle, Dublin 2
Tel 6770678
Seating 75/95
Open 8am-5pm Mon-Fri; 11.30-5pm Sat/Sun
Average £7.50; house wine (Cote du Rhone) £10.50, glass £1.75
Payment all major credit cards; EC, TC, LV.

This restaurant is situated at basement level just outside the walls of the old 13th-century fortress. The entire area has been the site of a recent archeological dig and the old building renovated and restored. The restaurant consists of three interlocking brightly

DUBLIN CASTLE

Founded by King John in 1205 and the seat of British rule until 1922, Dublin Castle is full of history and interest.

Guided tours take place from 10 am to 12 noon and from 2 pm to 5 pm every week day and from 2 pm to 5 pm at weekends.

The tours include the splendour of St. Patrick's Hall where President Robinson was inaugurated, the Throne Room where the throne presented by King William of Orange in 1692 is on display and a visit to the Undercroft where the remains of a medieval tower, part of the Old City Wall and the Castle Moat, are visible.

Also open to visitors are The Chapel Royal, The Roof Gardens, our Gift Shop and the Castle Vaults Restaurant.

Come up and see us, you won't be disappointed !

Dublin Castle can be accessed by pedestrians through the Palace Street Gate opposite the Olympia Theatre on Dame Street and the Corke Hill Gate beside City Hall.

decorated rooms the walls of which are hung with prints of the castle and memorabilia. The self-service menu includes freshly made sandwiches on wholemeal bread, a variety of salads, delicious soup, portions of smoked salmon as well as a wide range of hot meals like deep fried chicken, chicken wrapped in rashers in mustard sauce, beef pot, all served with potatoes and steamed vegetables. There are also homemade scones, apple tart and cakes - chocolate, carrot and walnut to name but a few. Unfortunately, decaffeinated coffee is not not served but you can have herbal teas. Clean pleasant surroundings and friendly staff carry your tray to a table. It provides an escape from the bustle of Dame Street and is a perfect conclusion of a tour.
Babies/children catered for, child portions; baby changing space in ladies' toilet. No smoking area (37/47). Tables outdoors. Private parties catered for by request. Takeaway. Ground floor.

Lane Gallery Restaurant
55 Pembroke Lane, Dublin 2
Tel 6611829/6762533
Seating 65
Open12.30pm-3pm Mon-Fri; 7.30pm-11.30pm Tues-Sat;
Average £16; £7.50 lunch; £19 dinner including wine; house wine £9.50. Fully licensed.
Payment all major credit cards; EC, TC.
In the heart of Georgian Dublin, the Lane Gallery is housed in an 18th-century coach house where the Duke of Wellington used to drink before setting out to hunt in the woods around the city. Artists exhibit their works and guests dine to the sound of traditional Irish music. After dinner, the resident pianist takes over and guests are invited to join in and sing.
Specialities are smoked and Barbary duck.
Babies/children catered for, child portions; baby changing room. Wheelchair friendly (except toilets). No smoking area (8). Booking advisable. Private room for parties. Neat casual dress. Takeaway by arrangement. Ground floor.

Hugh Lane Gallery Restaurant
The Municipal Gallery Of Modern Art
Charlemont House, Parnell Square, Dublin 1
Tel 8788238/8741903
Seating 70
Open 9.30am-5.30pm Tues-Fri; 9.30am-4.30pm Sat; 11am-4.30pm Sun; closed Mon
Average £4-4.50 main course; house wine ¼ bottle £1.85.
Payment A, V; EC, TC.
Charlemont House is one of Dublin's most elegant Georgian buildings. Huge Lane, successful art dealer and a nephew of Lady Gregory who died when the Lusitania was sunk in 1915, left the majority of his art collection to the National Gallery in London. A legal wrangle between London and Dublin evolved. Now 30 of the pictures remaining in Dublin include Monet's 'Vetheuil', Manet's 'Eva Gonzales' and Courbet's 'Snowstorm'. The self service restaurant serving healthy home-cooked food is ideal for lunch. Morning coffee or afternoon tea are pleasant alternatives. The cakes are all made by the lovely chef Esther who is renowned for her carrot cake. A speciality is homemade soup and vegetarian dishes are available.
Babies/children catered for, child portions; high chairs and baby changing room. No smoking area (40). Stairs.

Irish Film Centre
6 Eustace Street, Dublin 2
Tel 6778788/ (after 6pm) 6778099
Seating 60 upstairs restaurant; 60 bar/cafe
Open 12.30pm-11pm seven days
Average £10-12; £13-15 set three courses + coffee (weekends); house wine £8.95. Fully licensed.
Payment all major credit cards; TC, LV.
10% service for six or more.
This recently opened international restaurant is situated on the mezzanine overlooking the main hallway in the cinema, perfect for a meal either before or after a film and is a welcome change from the usual popcorn and ice-cream diet associated with a visit to the cinema. The menu changes daily both at lunchtime and in the evening,

with freshly cooked food of a high quality and very good value with emphasis on Irish ingredients. Sandwiches and cakes are available at lunchtime in the bar downstairs while the à la carte is served upstairs,
Babies/children catered for, child portions. No smoking area (4). Booking advisable. Tables oudoors and in foyer. Private parties catered for up to 200 buffet. Ground floor. First floor and stairs.

The Coffee Shop at IMMA
Royal Hospital Kilmainham, Dublin 8
Tel 6718666
Seating 110/250
Open 11am-4pm Tues-Sat; noon-5pm Sun; closed Mon
Average £5.80; £3.95 main course; house wine ¼ bottle £2.10. Cans/bottles beer, alcoholic and non-alcoholic.
Payment all major credit cards except DC; TC
Located in what used to be the service area of the Royal Hospital, the coffee shop here is down in the vaults. A self-service restaurant, it offers a minimum of two hot dishes and one vegetarian hot dish daily. Littl attention had been paid to quality anc standards here before recently but with a much more aggressive policy, standards have improved greatly.
Babies/children catered for, child portions; high chairs. No smoking area (36/83) Private room for parties, banqueting facilities. Takeaway sandwiches only. Basement. Stairs.

City Arts Centre Cafe
23/25 Moss Street, Dublin 2
Tel 6715907
Seating 80
Open 9.30am-10pm Mon-Sat
Average £5; house wine £8
Payment TC, LV.
This cafe, with enormous windows, has a view over the river Liffey that includes the magnificent Customs House. Bar floors and black-topped tables set a scene reminiscent of Paris with a blend of arty types and business people from surrounding offices and the IFSC across the river. Officially self-service, the helpful staff will bring dishes to

your table. A delicious lunch of samosa and salad with an acceptable dressing set us back £2. In the evening, the cafe becomes a theatre restaurant with the emphasis on the main course, wine and perhaps a platter of cheese. Lots of fun.

Babies/children catered for; high chairs. No smoking area (24). Takeaway. Ground floor. Stairs.

Winding Stair Bookshop Cafe

40 Lower Ormond Quay, Dublin 1
Tel 8733292
Seating 50
Open 10.30am-6pm Mon-Sat
Average £3-4. Unlicensed

Freshly prepared food in a bookshop is an interesting idea. All meat is additive-free and salads are organic. Adjacent to the Ha'penny Bridge, it commands a spectacular view of the Liffey. It should really be a stopover for all tourists who want to experience 'alternative Dublin'. Background music is mainly classical.

Babies/children catered for; baby changing room. Not wheelchair friendly. No smoking area (first floor). Takeaway. Stairs.

Bewley's Oriental Cafés Ltd

11 Westmoreland Street, Dublin 2
Tel 6776761

Dublin's Coffee & Rendezvous Emporium (Bewley's for short) has finally lived up to its reputation as an Oriental Coffee Shop and recently opened up in Tokyo! With four locations now in central-shopping Dublin and several more in the suburbs, Bewley's is as much part of the city's lore as Molly Malone. The definitive meeting place, and invariably packed to overflowing, the food, however, is decidedly mediocre. Bewley's Grafton Street is the flagship and operates on many different floors with frequent ventures into lunchtime theatre. Bewley's coffee is world renowned and served in many establishments outside its own. Cakes, pastries, bread and fresh coffee are also sold to take away just inside the doors at delicacy counters.

Tower Restaurant

IDA Enterprise Centre, Pearse Street, Dublin 2
Tel 6775655
Seating 75
Open 8am-5pm Mon-Fri, closed Sat/Sun
Average £4.95; £2.45 breakfast; house wine ¼ bottle £1.75.
Payment A, V; EC, TC, LV

Daytime self-service restaurant one of whose claims is their 'greaseless breakfast' which is grilled not fried. Lunches comprise dishes like beef and Guinness stew with vegetables, plaice au gratin, chicken kiev, lasagne and for the vegetarians, there are veggie burgers, all around £3.95. The decor is predominantly red with chinz table cloths and curtains. Specialising in Irish arts and crafts, the IDA Centre is a must for those souvenirs to take home. Don't be fooled by the smart shops, The Heritage Trail bus stops here and it's well worth the visit.

Babies/children catered for, child portions and menu; high chairs and baby changing room. No smoking area (60). Private room for parties by arrangement. Stairs. Takeaway.

Glitterati

Dubliners may be notoriously blasé about celebrities, nonetheless they enjoy being in the buzziest watering holes where choice tidbits of gossip are to be gleaned.

Fashionable eateries have waxed with the patronage of the glamorous and free-spending (not always the same thing), and waned when management forget that food and service do count even among the seriously social.

Some establishments, like the reliable and elegant Locks or the newish Commons with its drop-dead smart interior, inventive food and silky smooth service, have achieved their glitterdom through sheer excellence. Others attract the less sedate shakers and movers with streams of pop stars and wanabees enjoying good food at non-intimidating prices - Restaurant Tosca and Roly's Bistro are cases in point.

Places to see and be seen in may change overnight so those determined to be terminally trendy should watch the daily social columns.

Restaurant Tosca
20 Suffolk Street, Dublin 2
Tel 6796744
Seating 80
Open noon-midnight Sun-Wed; midnight last orders Thurs-Sat
Average £10; starters from £1.95
Payment all major credit cards except DC; TC, LV.
Everything about this restaurant is done with great taste - the decor combines metals and wood in sparse minimalist surroundings creating a clean, bright and trendy atmosphere. Lighting is suspended from steel wires above each table and is moveable, thus transforming the restaurant with ease. The food complements the surroundings, is very good and presented accordingly. Staff are friendly and the occasional Italian adds to its overall impression. For starters, the smoked fish salad at £3.50 is certainly good value. The pastas, as main courses - are served simply. Field mushrooms (£6.20) are big and luscious and come with a pasta of your choice; the pesto is good - lots of herbs and garlic and equally good value at £6.30. Sundried tomatoes (£6.30) are unusual and well worth a try. To accompany all the main courses, it is essential to try Tosca's bread from a variety including garlic (£1.75), tomato and mozzarella (£1.85), herb (£1.85) and plain at 70p. The desserts are equally good with a variety of exotics alongside old reliables. Decaffeinated coffee is also served.
Babies/children catered for, child portions; high chairs. No smoking area (40). Booking advisable. Private room for parties (Bono's). Takeaway by arrangement. Ground floor. Stairs down to toilets.

Trocadero
3 St Andrew's Street, Dublin 2
Tel 6775545/6799772
Seating 80
Open 6pm-12.15am Mon-Sat; 6pm-11.15pm Sun
Average £16; £8.50 pre-theatre; house wine £9.95. Fully licensed.
Payment all major credit cards
Seventeen years is a mighty long time in biz ... that's restaurant not show biz! though you'd be forgiven for mixing them up on a visit to The Troc. Dark with closeknit tables, the gallery of stars who've honoured this mystic eatery, festoon the walls with varying severities of attire and hair crop. Trocadero is a late post-theatre joint for the quixotic ... the food a necessary aside.
Babies/children catered for, child portions. Not wheelchair friendly. No smoking area (26). Booking advisable. Private room for parties up to 30. Neat casual dress. Ground floor. Stairs.

Ernie's Restaurant
Mulberry Gardens, Donnybrook, Dublin 4
Tel 2693300/2693260
Seating 60
Open 12.30pm-2.30pm Tues-Fri; 7.30pm-

10.30pm Tues-Sat
Average £30; £13.95 set lunch; £19.75 dinner; house wine £11.95. Fully licensed.
Payment all major credit cards; EC, TC.
12 ½% service.
French continental restaurant, Ernie's is well worth a visit - if you can find it! Mulberry Gardens, a street with no name, lies in the lane behind Kiely's pub. Follow the sign to the restaurant, then turn left. Named after Ernie Evans from Glenbeigh, Co.Kerry, whose pre-destined career in law came to an abrupt halt due to an accident, and who instead, studied cooking in Louisiana before going on to work in Stresa and in France. This incredible man opened the Donnybrook restaurant in 1984, a delightful place built around a garden courtyard, housing a fine art collection he put together himself. The food and ambience make this a very special hideaway and Robert is a genial and witty host. Michelin Guide and Egon Ronay. Specialities are grilled sole on the bone with bearnaise sauce and steak tartare. Vegetarian on request.
Babies/children catered for, child portions. Wheelchair friendly (except toilets). No smoking area (16). Booking essential. Can be booked for parties. Neat dress. Ground floor.

Dobbins
15 Stephen's Lane, Dublin 2
Tel 6764679/6613321
Seating 80
Open 12.30pm - 3pm Mon-Fri; 8pm - 11.30pm Tues-Sat
Average £20, £14.50 lunch; £19.50 dinner; house wine £12.50. Fully licensed.
Payment all major credit cards; EC, TC.
The rather grim alleyway looks like a shot out of a 1950s gangster film and the restaurant itself is housed in a long nissen hut type building which has been brilliantly disguised inside to resembles la cave of some grand château. As indeed there are on the wine list the product of many such caves. Now an institution, Dobbins is regularly featured in the media, probably because it is such a great favourite with Dublin's hacks. There is never any problem with your car as the obliging doorman will not only park it but will also retrieve it when you're ready to leave. While the food is good, it is not exceptional but with its sawdust-covered stone floors and popping champagne corks, it can be a pleasant place for an informal meal. Entertainment consists of live piano music Thursday-Saturday nights. Specialities are duck and lamb Vegetarian on request.
Babies/children catered for, child portions. No smoking area (20). Booking advisable. Private room for parties. Smart casual dress. Ground floor. Stairs.

Lock's Restaurant
1 Windsor Terrace, Portobello, Dublin 8
Tel 538352/543391
Seating 48
Open 12.30pm-2pm Mon-Fri; 7.15pm-11pm Mon-Sat; closed Sun.
Average £25, £12.95 lunch; £18.95 dinner; house wine £10.95.
Payment all major credit cards; EC, TC.
12½% service.
Brian Buckley, French trained, has been in situ here for the last four years. Locks is unexpectedly located on the Canal at Portobello in the site of a former pub-cum-shop of the old fashion. Its site and location, replete with Persian rugs, give the restaurant the homey feeling that entices diners back Large helpings and excellent service from a genial hostess help keep the occasion memorable.

Bon Appetit
9 James' Terrace, Malahide, Co Dublin
Tel 8450314
Seating 55
Open 12.30pm-2.30pm Mon-Fri; 7pm-11pm Mon-Sat; closed Sun and bank holidays
Average £25; £11 lunch; £20 table d'hote; house wine £9.50. Fully licensed.
Payment all major credit cards; EC, TC.
10% service.
Housed in an old Georgian terraced building in Malahide and poised on

Dublin's periphery is the Bon Appetit. The mood of this establishment is set by a rather olde worlde cosy interior, created by a Victorian floral wallpaper which at night is tempered by candles and soft light. Food is served by formally attired waiters and the menu, while continental, is aided by a mix of traditional and contemporary. Sole and escargots are highly favoured as are the turbot and duckling. They also offer a complete range of desserts, a fine conclusion to any meal.
Babies/children allowed early evening. No smoking area (20). Booking advisable. Private room for parties. Takeaway by arrangement. Collar and tie/elegant casual dress. Stairs.

La Stampa
35 Dawson Street, Dublin 2
Tel 6778611
Seating 180
Open noon-2.30pm, 6pm-11.30pm, midnight last orders Fri/Sat
Average £20; £16.50 table d'hote; £9.95 two course lunch; £12.95 three courses including coffee; house wine £10
Payment all major credit cards; EC, TC.
10% service for eight or more.
This restaurant with an elegant mirrored long dining-room has acquired a reputation for quality French style cuisine as well as some negative comments on the speed of service. Popular with the young and beautiful and the old and rich and just a stroll away from Leinster House, the clientele includes trendy TDs as well as senior civil servants. Because it is a short walk to The Pink Elephant or Lillie's Bordello, the trendiest nightspots, it is also frequented by musicians, film stars and models. Not really the place for a secret tryst, it is ideal for an outrageously lavish celebration. Specialities are fish soup and lobster ravioli. Vegetarian available.
Babies/children allowed; high chairs. Wheelchair friendly upstairs. No smoking area (10). Private room available for parties. Steps up front. Stairs to toilets.

Roches Bistro
12 New Street, Malahide, Co Dublin
Tel 8452777
Seating 26
Open noon-2.30pm Tues-Sat; 6pm-10.30pm Thurs-Sat.
Average £20; £18.95 table d'hote dinner; lunch special £10.95; house wine £9.95.
Payment all major credit cards; EC, TC.
Service charge for eight or more.
Conveniently located in the centre of the charming maritime village of Malahide, less than a quarter of an hour from Dublin, Roches provides a quiet refuge from the demands of city life, offering a fine blend of French cuisine in an aura of Gaelic surroundings. Its inner intimacy is enhanced by clean white walls adorned with continental prints and a tasteful array of antiques. An open fire encourages diners to sit and watch their meal being prepared. Variety and diversification make for a menu that is never boring. Included here are starting gems like mousseline of scallops and for entrées, their duck dishes are highly

recommended. The food is delicious and combines a subtle blend of simplicity and sophistication.
Babies/children catered for, child portions. Wheelchair friendly (except toilets). No smoking area (8). Booking advisable. Takeaway for breads only.

George's Bistro
29 South Frederick Street, Dublin 2
Tel 6797000/6797560
Open 12pm-1pm Mon-Fri, 7pm-1am Tues-Sat.
Average £22; £7.75 lunch; £18.50 dinner; house wine £10 (lunchtime), £13.50
Payment all major credit cards; EC, LV and TC.
In business for the last ten years, George's is best described as a party restaurant. Arrive at 9, dine, then enjoy the blues or jazz which starts at 10. Later on, stand up and belt out your party piece or watch in awe (and sometimes horror) as others - the occasional politician or celebrity - do. Not the place for serious conversation; food takes a back seat to lively spontaneous entertainment of another sort entirely. Specialities are salmon en croute and monkfish. Vegetarian on request. Egon Ronay.
Babies/children welcome early evening. Not wheelchair friendly. No smoking area. (25). Booking advisable.

Roly's Bistro
7 Ballsbridge Terrace, Dublin 4
Tel 6682611
Seating 120
Open noon-3pm, 6pm-10pm Mon-Sat; 6pm-9.30pm Sun.
Average £15-17 dinner; £9.50 table d'hote lunch; house wine £8.50, glass £2. Fully licensed.
Payment all major credit cards.
10% service charge distributed among staff.
The eating resort of the moment, Roly's boasts a truly massive operation employing some 50 full-time and 25 part-time staff, among them no less than 17 chefs. It sees the marriage of the eponymous maitre d' Roly Saul to chef de cuisine Colin O'Daly, former of The Park, Blackrock, long a celebrity in the Dublin culinary world. It has to be one of the biggest dining successes ever in Dublin - since its opening around Christmas last year, it hasn't had one vacant seat (lunch or dinner) and bookings, needless to say, must be made two/three months in advance. The formula? Build a restaurant from the ground to your exact specifications in a desirable, just south-of-centre location; blend the talents and tentacles of two well-renowned, well-seasoned restaurateurs, employ about 50 tune-whistling but efficiently pleasant hell-raisers to make the place feel like downtown Tokyo during rush-hour, offer a wide-ranging bistro menu of excellent value (lunch just £9.50) in bright airy surroundings, feature your front on the cover of **Edibilia**.
No smoking area (30). Booking essential. Private parties between 20-60. Casual smart dress.

Grey Door, Blushes Bistro
22-23 Upper Pembroke Street, Dublin 2
Tel 6763286
Seating 65 Grey Door; 60 Blushes
Open 12.30pm-2.15pm Mon-Fri; 7pm-11pm Mon-Sat - Grey Door; 12.30pm-2.15pm, 6pm-11.30pm Mon-Sat - Blushes; closed Sun.
Average £22 ; £15 lunch - Grey Door; £14 three courses; £14 lunch - Blushes; house wine £10.95.
Fully licensed
Payment all major credit cards, EC, LV.
12 1/2% service.

Within walking distance of St Stephen's Green, the Grey Door provides a rare amalgam of Nordic and Russian viands. The unique culinary style and Georgian elegance produce an inner harmony, enlivened by its refined furnishings. The courtly tune continues with amiable and traditionally clad staff who make diners feel as though they were very special guests. The basement of this building also houses Blushes Bistro, a less formal small restaurant and upstairs additionally provides a beautiful room set aside for private dining. Dishes to be savoured at The Grey Door include Beef Novgorod and gravlax - cured salmon, accompanied by a light mustard sauce and dill potatoes. The wine list will tempt even the most discerning connoisseur.

Babies/children allowed. Not wheelchair friendly. No smoking area (21) Grey Door; (20) Blushes. Booking advisable. Private room for parties. Takeaway by arrangement. Tie required Grey Door. Ground floor. Stairs.

Granny's Restaurant
8 Ely Place, Dublin 2
Tel 6760044
Seating 45
Open 12.30pm-2.30pm, 6pm-11pm Tues-Sat; closed Mon
Average £15.00; £7,95 four course set lunch; £9.95 early bird four courses 6pm-8pm; house wine £9.95.
Payment all major credit cards; EC, TC.
10% service for ten or more.

Situated in the basement of one of the finest Georgian houses in Dublin, owned by the Knights of Columbanus, Granny's is directly adjacent to Lower Baggot Street and St Stephen's Green. A Mediterranean style entrance leads into a small intimate oval shaped winebar/reception area which features a high vaulted ceiling. Oak half-panelled walls as well as a blazing fire in the 18th-century fireplace give it a comfortable club-like ambience The conservative menu features seafood parcels, rack of lamb stuffed roast pork, salmon with dill sauce and fillet steak. The wine list is good - all reasonably priced with no shocks.

Babies/children not encouraged but catered for Not wheelchair friendly. Booking advisable Function rooms for private parties. Basement.

The Alexandra Restaurant
Earlsfort Terrace, Dublin 2
Tel 6765555
Seating 45
Open 12.30pm-2pm Mon-Fri; 7pm-10.30pm Mon-Sat; closed Sun.
Average £27.40; £15.95 lunch; £22.50 dinner; house wine £12. Fully licensed.
Payment all major credit cards; EC, TC, LV.
15% service.

Dining here is less a meal than an event Advice not to hurry or to pricewatch must be heeded - anything less than two and a half hours is a waste of time and money Seafood dominates the menu with main courses in the £16 category whilst seafood ragout (£9.25) is tipped as a starter to savour For such a serious dining experience (dadowood surrounds, best cloth napkins and oodles of the best silver cutlery impeccable glassware), it comes as a nice surprise that the staff, while the odds are stacked in favour of imported French snobs or catwalkers filling time between assignments, are the best of Dublin with disarming accent and hospitality Somewhere to dress up for and better still, if you are someone's guest.

Babies/children allowed; high chairs and baby changing room. Booking essential. Private room for parties of ten. Smart dress. Ground floor.

Polo One Restaurant
5-6 Molesworth Place, Dublin 2
Tel 6766442/6763362
Seating n/a
Open 12.30pm-2pm, 7pm-11pm Mon-Sat
Average £22 ; £12.95 table d'hote lunch; house wine £10.
Payment all major credit cards.
A lovely restaurant with white brick walls and lots of pictures, its window sills full of plants plus a highly polished clay tile floor and open fire. All tables are covered with crisp white tablecloths and monogrammed matching napkins.The olive, tomato and mozzarella salad is a crisp way to start the meal. Honey-glazed guinea fowl with mango, ginger and olive sauce with just a hint of curry is an interesting combination. Desserts include an interesting strawberry torte.
Babies/ children catered for; high chairs and baby changing room. No smoking area. Booking advisable. Takeaway by arrangement. Ground floor.

QV2
14-15 St Andrew's Street, Dublin 2
Tel 6773363/6772246
Seating 100
Open noon-3pm, 6pm-12.30pm Mon-Sat; closed Sun
Average £15-20; tourist menu; house wine £9.50. Fully licensed.
Payment all major credit cards; EC, LV.
10% service for eight or more.
The sequel to the Quo Vadis restaurant, QV2 faces stiff competition here with no less than six restaurants and two pubs flanking this brief sliproad. If the Troc across the street requires even the hardiest of dudes to remove their shades then, by contrast, in QV2 you can keep them on. Light and bright with a welcoming air, when the place is really singing, it's almost as loud as a Lansdowne roar (Oops! almost said Hill 16!) Starters range from soup at £1.95 to crab claws at £5.25. A small selection of pastas weigh in at average £6.50, while main courses - a broad brush of game, fowl and vegetarian - range from £8-£11. Caveat emptor - extras like mixed salad, vegetables or selected potatoes, jack up the price by another £2. As supporters of the arts, the restaurant has something of a rich theatre feel to it. Jazz music downstairs at weekends, with wine and friends, can transport a mood far outside Dublin. Specialities are duck, fish and lamb. Vegetarian available.
Babies/children catered for; high chairs. Not wheelchair friendly. No smoking area. Booking advisable. Private room for parties up to 40. Ground floor. Basement. Stairs down.

The Commons Restaurant
Newman House, 85-86 St. Stephen's Green, Dublin 2.
Tel 4752597
Seating 50
Open 12.30pm-2.15pm Mon-Fri; 7pm-10pm Mon-Sat
Average £32.50; £16 set lunch; £27.50 table d'hote dinner; house wine £11. Fully licensed
Payment all major credit cards; EC. 15% service.
The restaurant is in the basement of Newman House, the original house of UCD, which is classical Georgian. 85 was built in 1738 and 86 in 1765. As a tribute to James Joyce who was educated upstairs, the elegant restaurant downstairs houses a collection of twelve paintings by Irish artists. Jerry the chef, who has worked all over the world, uses his experience to come up with an original cuisine on the nouvelle style using mainly Irish produce of the best quality. A haven for pinstripes during lunch, a banker for corporate entertainment (or indeed to very impress the significant other) sees a sense of proper decorum in the place. This restaurant, I might add, the old canteen for UCD, will bring back happy memories for many an old student. Specialities are seafood and game. Vegetarian available.
Not wheelchair friendly. No smoking area (25). Booking essential. Tables outdoors in Iveagh Gardens. Private room for parties. Smart dress. Basement. Stairs.

Cooke's Cafe
14 South William Street, Dublin 2
Tel 6790536/6790538
Open 8am-midnight Mon-Fri; 12 noon-3pm, 6pm-midnight Sat/Sun.
Average £22; £7 minimum; £5breakfast; £11.95 lunch; house wine £9.95.
Payment all major credit cards
Based in the heart of Dublin's fashion district, it's no surprise that designers and journalists are seen lunching here daily. Cal-Ital food and delicious exotic breads are served against a backdrop of Italianate murals. Dining at Cooke's functions like an Armani suit and Gucci shoes: there to be noticed but must not be the centre of attention. The feel-good factor is high with pavement dining by day if the weather is nice and classical guitar at night. Specialities are seafood, Mediterranean. Vegetarian on request. Not cheap but if your budget runs to it, well worth a try.
Babies/children catered for; child portions. Wheelchair friendly (except for toilets). No smoking area (6). Takeaway by arrangement. Booking essential. Tables outdoors. Ground floor. Stairs down

Cooke's Bakery,
31 Francis Street, Dublin 8,
supplies both wholesale and retail with a full selection of interesting breads - foccaccia, aubergine, olive - as well as desserts and pastries.

Old Dublin Restaurant
90-91 Francis Street, Dublin 8
Tel 542028/542346
Seating 65
Open12.30pm-2.30pm Mon-Fri; 6pm-11pm Mon-Sat
Average £19; £11.50 lunch; £10 pre-theatre 6pm-7pm; house wine £10.75. Fully licensed.
Payment all major credit cards; EC, TC.
This restaurant, a longtime favourite inner city restaurant, is located on a main thoroughfare in the heart of medieval Dublin, adjacent to Christchurch and close to St. Patrick's Cathedral. It is a welcoming well-illuminated establishment with an elegant intimate and tastefully furnished interior which is warmed by red tablecloths and starched linen napkins. The widely varied menu reflects Scandinavia's strong emphasis on seafood with gravlax (marinated salmon), fish blinis and ragout of seafood or less usual entrees would be grilled monkfish Nicolai and veal kidneys Desna. There are fine selections of both desserts and wines, the latter varying considerably more in price.
Babies/children catered for, child portions and menu on request. Wheelchair friendly (except toilets). No smoking area (24). Booking advisable. Neat casual dress. Takeaway by arrangement. Ground floor. Stairs.

Garibaldi's
Crown Alley, Dublin 2
Tel 6717288
Seating 113
Open noon-midnight Mon-Sat; 1pm-11pm Sun.
Average £13; house wine carafe £9.25; ½ £4.75.
Payment all major credit cards except DC; EC, TC, LV.
Located opposite the Rock Garden on one of the busiest thoroughfares in the heart of Dublin's most throbbing activity centre, Garibaldi's doesn't brag. It doesn't have to with the volume of traffic through its doors. Prices are extremely competitive and a good basic range of food - pastas, chargrills, seafood, pizzas - is of superior quality. A three-storey restaurant, it has a broad appeal that attracts professionals and clerks as well as those 'resting' between assignments. Staff are on a constant keep-fit programme up and down stairs. It appears as ideally suited to power lunches as it does to romancers' rendezvous with a certain aura promoting relaxation and comfort to all classes.
Babies/children catered for, child portions and menu; high chairs. Wheelchair friendly (ground floor only). No smoking area (20). Booking advisable. Tables outdoors (12-15). Private floors to hire for parties. Takeaway by arrangement. Three levels. Stairs.

The Buttery Brasserie
Royal Hibernian Way, Dublin 2
Tel 6796259
Seating 75
Open 9am-8pm Mon-Sat (food); 10.30am-11.30pm seven days (bar).
Average £10; £7.95 lunch; £3.50 breakfast; house wine £7.95. Fully licensed.
Payment all major credit cards; EC, TC.
10% service.
The Buttery Brasserie is a restaurant not a pub. It's a gathering point during the day in this busy pedestrian precinct where those who've just popped out of Anndress or Presents of Mind or purchased their week's supply of Leonidas chocolate across the way might decide to have a chat and a bite, or indeed just a quick bevvy. At night, it's young and beautiful (and smokey) and food is slightly de-emphasised.
Babies/children catered for up to 7pm, child portions; high chairs and baby changing room. No smoking area (10). Booking advisable 1pm-3pm. Tables outdoors. Private room for parties. Takeaway by arrangement. Ground floor.

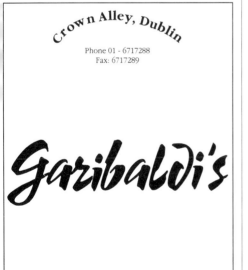

Pretenders

The buzz restaurants come and go - nowhere faster than in Dublin - and some hover on the edge of glitterdom for years. Many of the restaurants in this section are in difficult-to-define categories. perhaps waiting to be elevated to total stardom - only time will tell.

The Cottonwood Cafe is on the site of several lively predecessors, all heavy on music and last-gasp street fashion. Clarets in Blackrock is rather more staid, stars an acclaimed young chef, and is seen by some as the natural inheritor of Colin O'Daly's clientele. Different again is Ryan's of Parkgate Street, the fine old Victorian pub whose upstairs restaurant goes from strength to strength with fresh, stylish and beautifully presented food and a superb wine list.

This section could be retitled 'The upwardly and downwardly mobile'. Watch this space.

Bia
Blooms Hotel
Anglesea Street, Temple Bar, Dublin 2
Tel 6715622
Seating 70
Open 12.30pm-2pm Mon-Fri; 5pm-10.15pm Mon-Sat; 9.15pm last orders Sun
Average £10-12; £4.50 set lunch; house wine £8.50 (less expensive options available). Fully licensed.
Payment all major credit cards; EC, TC, LV. 12% service.
In the centre of Dublin's 'Latin Quarter' - Temple Bar and close to the River Liffey, the Bia Restaurant in Blooms Hotel is bright, spacious and modern. Well chosen paintings adorn the walls and the menu offers a wide choice. Rolls beautifully fresh, butter curled and not too soft. Recommended is the ravioli filled with Irish cheese and served in rich tomato and basil sauce as are delicate baked paupiettes of sole stuffed with spinach and smoked salmon and served with choice of assorted potatoes. Dessert portions not overgenerous. Unlimited cafetiere coffee at £1 per head is a praiseworthy touch. Vegetarian on request.
Babies / children catered for, child portions; high chairs and baby changing room in hotel. Not really wheelchair friendly. Booking advisable. Air conditioned. Private parties catered forup to 30. First floor. Stairs and lift.

Buck's Bistro
26-30 Upper Rathmines Road, Rathmines, Dublin 6
Tel 976095
Seating 70
Open pasta shop 5.30pm-11pm Sun-Thurs; bistro 5.30pm-12pm Sun-Sat
Average £10; £9.95 early bird 6pm-8pm; house wine £8.70.
Payment all major credit cards.
A cosy black and white, timbered dining area, Bucks Bistro is attached to 'Uppercross House', a small but very comfortable guesthouse. By the way, 'Uppercross' was the old name for Rathmines. Specialities: fish, steak and vegetarian dishes.
Babies/children catered for, child portions and menu; high chairs and baby changing room. No smoking area (12). Booking advisable at weekends. Takeaway by arrangement. Ground floor. Stairs.

Cottonwood Cafe
7 Johnsons Court, Westbury Mall, Dublin 2
Tel 6712276
Seating 100
Open 9am-11.30pm six days; closed Sun.
Average £9.00 evening meal, £6.50 daytime; £3.95 set price meals (all lunches include a free glass of wine); house wine £8.95.
Payment A, V; EC, LV.
I remember it as The Colony which begat The Wildebeast, then voted Best Nighttime restaurant by In Dublin, which begat the current Cottonwood Cafe, still under the supervision of Joe and Aisling Murphy. This is a speakeasy which tolerates a lot of

messin'. It is really two restaurants wrapped into one, located in Johnson's Court, that shady alley between Grafton Street and the Powerscourt Townhouse. A relaxed self-service eatery with a regular menu that also caters for vegetarians by day, a metamorphosis to table service with the addition of pizza, pasta and burgers occurs, beginning at 6pm. Live jazz, blues and rock at weekends further recline the mood and upgrade the Fun Factor.
Babies/children catered for, child portions. Wheelchair friendly (except toilets). No smoking area (20). Booking advisable. Tables outdoors during summer. Private parties available. Ground floor. Stairs to toilets.

Claret's Restaurant
63/65 Main Street, Blackrock, Co Dublin
Tel 2882008
Seating 60
Open 12.30pm-2.30pm Tues-Fri; 7pm-10pm Tues-Sat;
Average £30; £12.95 set three course lunch + coffee; £22.95 table d'hote; house wine £11.25.
Payment all major credit cards except DC; EC, TC.
Slightly off the beaten track, the dining area in this family-run restaurant, basically one large room, is cleverly divided into two levels and an irregular shape provides corners that create an unusual amount of privacy. The menu changes rather frequently at Clarets and can include impressive starters like a mousseline of seafood with a light ginger sauce and a fleuron of puff pastry. Their homemade breads, including gluten-free for coeliacs, are unusual and very good. Game in season is a speciality and an example would be pigeon in a rich port sauce - succulent breast wrapped first in cabbage, then filo pastry and baked. Steamed supreme of turbot is also worthy of mention - a huge tender fillet with a grainy mustard sauce and garnished with leeks, courgettes and carrots. Desserts like a tangy lemon tart and house speciality banana and almond parfait are delicious and good coffee and imaginative petits fours round off a most enjoyable meal of the best

seasonal food cooked to a high standard. Specialities - game in season, also fish. Vegetarian available.
No smoking area (15). Booking advisable, essential at the weekends. Casual smart dress. Ground floor. Stairs.

Terrace Bistro
Earlsfort Centre, Leeson Street, Dublin 2
Tel 6610585
Seating 40
Open 12.15pm-2.15pm Mon-Fri and Sun; 6.30pm-9.30pm Mon-Sat.
Average £11.50 dinner; £7.50 lunch; £6.50 breakfast; £4 continental breakfast; £8.50 house wine.
Payment all major credit cards; EC, TC.
The Terrace Bistro, part of Stephen's Hall Hotel, is very comfortable with warm ochre walls, lots of brightly coloured pictures, linen tablecloths and fresh flowers on each table. A thoroughly pleasant restaurant, attached to a concept hotel consisting of apartments - bedroom, sitting room and kitchen for the same price as the better hotels in the area. The menu is imaginative - an assortment of not obviously complementary flavours are successfully combined; presentation gets top marks and prices are keen for what's on offer. Standards are well above habitual hotel fare. Specialities include basket of seafood with vegetables, stuffed supreme of chicken with hazelnut mousseline and there are vegetarian options.
Babies/children catered for, child portions and menu to order; high chairs and baby changing room. No smoking area (8). Booking advisable. Tables outdoors. Private room for parties. Takeaway by arrangement. Stairs. Lift.

Turrets Restaurant
Eleanora's Pub
147/149 Drimnagh Road, Dublin 12
Tel 558887
Seating 58
Open 6pm-11pm Wed-Sun; noon-5pm Sunday lunch
Average £12; £7.95 Sunday lunch; house wine £7.95. Fully licensed

Payment A, V; EC (food), TC.

Although Drimnagh is not exactly the dining centre of Dublin, there is a little surprise for those who find this comfortable restaurant with an olde worlde atmosphere upstairs in Eleanora's Pub. The menu too is unusual with starters like Szechuan style crab claws with garlic and chillies and deep fried mushrooms in garlic mayonnaise.

The main courses range from traditional chicken kiev and roast lamb to the exotic jumbo prawns in a Pernod and butter sauce. Their desserts are also recommended and cocktails are available on request.

Specialities are steak and duckling. Vegetarian on request.

Babies/children catered for up to 8pm, child portions and menu; high chairs and changing room. Not wheelchair friendly. No smoking area (28). Tables outdoors. Dress neat casual. Stairs.

Le Coquillage

Shopping Centre, Blackrock, Co. Dublin

Tel 2883470

Seating 60

Open 8am-10pm Tues-Sat; 8am-6.30pm Mon; closed Sun

Average £8.50 lunch; £10. dinner; £2 minimum noon-2.30pm; £3.95 main course special lunch; house wine £8.95. glass £1.85.

Payment all major credit cards except AmEx; EC, TC, LV.

International restaurant also serves morning coffee and afternoon tea. Pleasant decor - lead lit ceiling with French quarry-tiled floor and a terracotta look surround the serving area bordering the open kitchen. View over Dublin Bay makes a romantic setting for a candlelit dinner. Speciality: pfannkuchen (German pancakes with savoury stuffing and seafood). Vegetarian available.

Babies/children catered for, child portions; high chairs and baby changing room in Centre. Wheelchair friendly at lunchtime. No smoking area (12). Booking advisable at weekends. Tables outdoors. Restaurant can be taken over for private parties. Takeaway by arrangement. Tie at dinner. Stairs.

Ryan's of Parkgate Street

28 Parkgate Street, Dublin 8

Tel 6776097/6719352

Seating 32

Open12.30pm-2.30pm Mon-Fri; 7pm-10pm Tues-Sat; closed Sun

Average £20; £13 lunch; house wine £9.95. Fully licensed.

Payment all major credit cards except AmEx, EC, TC. 10% service for ten or more.

Ryans of Parkgate Street is one of Dublin's finest Victorian pubs, the present building dating back to 1896. The central bar is mahogany and houses a double-faced clock. As pubs of this era were also shops, there are tea and sugar drawers behind the bar. The restaurant does not serve typical 'pub food'. This is a dining-room with interesting pictures on the walls and linen-dressed tables. The menu includes feuilletes of chicken with tiger prawns and other international dishes. Specialities are fresh seafood and fine meats. Vegetarian on request.

Babies/children allowed up to 7pm. Not wheelchair friendly. No smoking area (8). Booking advisable. Stairs.

MacNabs

1/2 Trinity Street, Dublin 2

Tel 6799796

Seating 40

Open 7.30am-4pm Mon-Fri; 8.30am-5pm Sat; in process of opening late

Average £10; £2 minimum lunch time; house wine £9.45.

Payment LV.

Formerly known as The Jazzerie (a popular lunchtime premises), this location has metamorphosed into a day and evening opening with a wide menu under the supervision of the masterminds of the now defunct Kilmartin's Wine Bar, Baggot Street. The label of 'lunchtime only' is difficult to erase as MacNabs tries to establish credible evening trade. Starter average is £3, main courses £7 and pastas £6 - selection is still fairly limited and un-earth shattering but, given time, I'm sure greatness will evolve. Entertainment consists of piped jazz.

Vegetarian available.
Babies/children catered for. Wheelchair friendly (except toilets). No smoking area (14). Takeaway. Ground floor. Stairs down to toilets.

Ivy Court Restaurant
88 Rathgar Road, Dublin 6
Tel 920633/4
Seating 85
Open 5.30pm-11.30pm seven days; 5.30pm-11pm Sun.
Average £14; house wine £9.50, glass £2.20.
Payment A, V; EC, TC.
10% service for ten or more.
This restaurant is in a two-storey converted house. The chef proprietor is Swiss and this is reflected in the rustic murals. The menu offers an enormous choice - there are 21 starters and an almost equal number of main courses. A speciality is muscargot which is principally mushrooms stuffed with crabmeat and mussels and baked with cheese and garlic butter. It also prides itself on its sirloin steak Cafe de Paris. Basically, prices are below average, yet the cuisine appears to be above average - a good combination in these times.
Babies/children allowed up to 7pm. No smoking area (12). Booking advisable. Casual neat dress. Ground floor. Stairs.

Tá Sé Mahogani Gaspipes
17 Manor Street, Dublin 7
Tel 6798138
Seating 40
Open noon-3pm Tues-Fri; 7pm-midnight Tues-Thurs; 7pm-2am Fri-Sat; closed Sun/Mon.
Average £13; house wine £8.95.
Payment all major credit cards except AmEx; EC, TC.
If nothing else, the name of this restaurant will make you curious to visit it. However, there is a lot to make you return again and again. Apart from food, there is a very heavy emphasis on music with nightly jazz sessions featuring guests like Louis Stewart. An extremely friendly host pulls up a chair to your table to go through the day's specials (of which there are many). These include a wide range of Chinese and American style dishes - the usual burgers served with French fries and a side salad. The chicken satay is very good, served with three pancakes, sauce in one bowl, vegetables in another and meat in a third. These you mix as you wish and roll in the pancakes. For dessert, chocolate brownies are good but highly calorific and served with a huge dollop of cream. Nice touches include finger bowls and jellybabies instead of mints as you leave!!
Babies/children tolerated and catered for, child portions. No smoking area (10). Booking advisable. Tables outdoors. Ground floor. Stairs.

Canaletto's
69 Mespil Road, Dublin 4
Tel 6785084
Seating 60
Open 8am-12.30am Mon-Sat; 6pm-12.30am Sun
Average £17 dinner; £5 set lunch; £2 afternoon tea; house wine £9.50.
Payment all major credit cards; EC, TC, LV.
Nice pun in operation here, disguising this clever little restaurant opposite the Canal in the middle of officeland off Baggot Street. With an international menu tending toward Italian, the atmosphere is unforced, casual and friendly. Terry, once head chef in Mountjoy jail, has cooked for twelve years all over Europe with distinguished guests including Major Ronald Ferguson (distinguished?) and the Princess of Wales. The restaurant is divided in twain - a languid ground floor leads to an arty, close-knit basement. The staff are almost horizontal they're so laid-back, yet still maintain a tight grip. Plenty of pasta, salads, pancakes and fish, lovingly prepared. Simple well-priced food at lunchtime and all available to go. Lunch at £4-5 is worth a detour even if you're not in the neighbourhood.
Babies/children catered for, child portions and menu. Wheelchair friendly (except toilets). Booking advisable. Private room for parties. Takeaway. Ground floor. Stairs.

River Moon Cafe
23/24 Wellington Quay, Temple Bar, Dublin 2
Tel 6719113/6719114
Seating 110
Open 12.30pm-11pm Mon-Thurs; 12.30pm-midnight Fri/Sat; 5.30pm-10.30pm Sun.
Average £11; house wine carafe £9.95; corkage £3.50 special occasions, beer and wine.
Payment A, V; EC, TC.
10% service for eight or more.
Surprisingly under-exposed quayside venue, this sister of the Little Moon is older, more mature and very attractive. Colour and layout are inviting while upstairs by the window provides a beautiful view of the Liffy at night. The menu, illustrated by the ubiquitous Cathy Dineen, reflects a fairly mixed bag - Greek and French starters (£1.95-3.95) with fish, meat, burgers and vegetarian main courses (£4.95-7.95). Food quality is consistently good, atmosphere is superb; outdoor dining is very conceivable (weather permitting). Underestimated at present - catch it before it gets trendy!
Babies/children catered for, child portions. Not wheelchair friendly. No smoking area (18). Booking advisable. Tables outdoors. Private room for parties. Takeaway. Ground floor. Stairs.

The Little Moon
12 Fownes Street, Temple Bar, Dublin 2
Tel 6776111
Seating 68
Open 12.30pm-11pm Mon-Thurs; 12.30pm-11.30pm Fri/Sat; 12.30pm-10.30pm Sun.
Average £10; house wine £8.95.
Payment A. 10% service for eight or more.
A new restaurant on the block, Little Moon replaces the old Pastra Nostra yet retains a lot of its interior charm. Very summery with windows wide open in clement weather, the menu takes you on a whistle-stop global tour, trying its hand as master of all trades. Its international selection ranges from Greek, Japanese (teriyaki, tofu), Indian, Spanish, French, Israeli, Portuguese to even incorporate the US (credited with spareribs). Dishes range from starters averaging £2.50 to main courses either £4.95 or £5.95. Establishing itself, it's got a tougher task than G7 trade negotiations.
Babies/children catered for, child portions. No smoking area (12). Booking advisable for eight or more. Tables outdoors. Takeaway by arrangement. Ground floor. Stairs.

Plurabelle Brasserie
Hotel Conrad, Earlsfort Terrace, Dublin 2
Tel 6765555
Seating 95
Open 7am-11.30pm seven days.
Average £12.50; house wine £12. Fully licensed.
Payment all major credit cards; EC, TC, LV.
15% service.
The lighter side of dining at the Conrad, the Plurabelle, masquerading as a brasserie, is bright and airy with well-spaced tables. The menu is fairly wide-ranging - salads (£7-8.50), sandwiches (£4.65), seafood (£7-10.75) and meat catering for a particularly busy lunchtime trade. Breakfast refreshingly, and served from 7am, is open to the public. Another unsuual feature is the facility for National Concert Hall goers to order their starter/main course before the concert then return for dessert and coffee. For some strange reason, you must pay before dessert!
Babies/children catered for , child portions; high chairs and baby changing room (bedroom). No smoking area (50). Booking advisable. Air conditioned. Neat casual dress. Ground floor. Lift from car park.

Wright's Brasserie
11-12a The Crescent, Monkstown, Co. Dublin
Tel 2805174/2841693
Seating 90
Open noon-3pm, 6pm-11pm Mon-Sat; closed Sun
Average £13 four course dinner; £9.95 four course lunch ; house wine £8.75, glass £1.80.
Payment all major credit cards; EC, TC, LV.
Skylit, clubable haunt that is divided into bar and restaurant menu - snacks and the formal substantial. Menu is fairly adventurous and very reasonably priced - poultry, fish, pasta and meals are served both in the dining hall or the trendier wine-bar area.

Babies/children catered for, child portions and lunch menu. No smoking area (22). Tables outdoors (weather permitting!) Private room for parties. Takeaway. Ground floor.

Oscars of Hollywood Bistro
103 Morehampton Road, Donnybrook, Dublin 4
Tel 6601872
Seating 40
Open 12.30pm-3.30pm, 6.30pm-11.30pm Tues-Sun; closed Mon.
Average £15; house wine £9.50, ½ bottle £5.75.
Payment A, V; EC, TC. 10% service.
A relatively new bistro to open in Donnybrook with a classical Hollywood theme. The photo stills decorating the walls will be admired by film buffs. B/w stills (about 140) match the floor tiles; chairs are moulded director's chairs with the names of film stars etched on the back. Soup (varies daily) costs £1.85, while main courses vary in price from £5.95 for barbecued spareribs to £10.90 for crispy duckling. One caveat is that you must add extras like salad and vegetables at £1.25 and up. Atmosphere, however, is very laid-back as is the service. A unique touch is the offering of a full bottle of wine where two or more people are concerned with a counter-credit for any undrunk - no doubt an incitement to finish the first bottle.
Babies/children catered for, child portions. No smoking area (4). Booking advisable for large groups (22/24). Ground floor.

Old Reliables

There are times when the familiar, tried and true are just the ticket. This is when the solid restaurant purveyors of steak and mom's apple pie come into their own. With no pretentions to Franglais menus, fruit flavoured vinegars, or plaited fish on berry coulis, these stalwarts are popular scenes of First Communion and Confirmation parties.

With catering that pleases youngsters as well as doting grandparents, in-betweeners and non-celebrants are lured by the relaxed atmosphere - the sort of place where daytime pinstripers appear in pullovers and comfy loafers, when cooking at home just isn't worth the bother.

Many of these restaurants are located in the suburbs, with old-timers like the Pronto Grill in Ranelagh seeing student patrons returning with second and third generations of young snappers.

Blakes Restaurant
The Grove, Stillorgan, Co Dublin
Tel 2887678
Seating 260
Swords Road, Whitehall, Dublin 9
Tel 367333
Seating 240
Open noon - midnight seven days.
Average £13.50; £4 minimum; £5.95 set price; house wine £7.95, glass £1.75.
Payment A, V; EC, TC, LV

Blakes is a little like McDonald's - whether you love it or hate it, you can't ignore the fact that it's a formula that works, and must keep the owners smiling. Their Stillorgan flagship has been lifted and settled on the Swords Road (northside) where it's beginning to thrive. Blakes caters for all types and age groups i e the mass market and at anytime at either location, you will witness families, Communion and Confirmation clobber, business meetings, romancers, travellers, mobiles, country folk. Their menu vies with the Footplate for award of 'Largest Laminated Menu' and its content is bland and varied - designed to cater for all tastes. A practicable assortment of seafood, chicken, steaks, desserts that may have appeared on an Irish menu of 20 years ago is however peppered with up-to-date icons like a decent range of vegetarian dishes (£5.75) and cafetiere coffee (decaff is also available), good value at 95p. One very signficant feature about Blakes is the perennial chirpiness of its staff who are well-trained, polite and eager-to-please with an excellent telephone manner. The formula is right here - serve the masses a good variety of what they want (i e solid, decent food) at the right prices in sufficient quantites with a few concessions to enlarging markets in a friendly manner ... you know, for the trade secrets alone, restaurateurs should pay more for this book. (N B Prices for Swords Road approximately 10% lower than Stillorgan).

Babies/children catered for, child menu; high chairs and changing rooms. No smoking area (70

Stillorgan; 75 Swords Road). Booking advisable for six or more. Parties catered for in Stillorgan. Takeaway by arrangement. Ground floor.

The Brokers Restaurant
25 Dame Street, Dublin 2
Tel 6793534
Seating 60
Open midday-midnight seven days
Average £9.50; house wine £8.95, glass £1.85. Fully licensed.
Payment A, V; EC, TC. 10% service
Informal restaurant opened two years. Vegetarian food available.
Babies/children catered for, child portions. No smoking area (30). Booking advisable. Two sections of restaurant available for parties. Stairs to toilets.

Patricks Restaurant
Comans Pub
2/4 Terenure Road East, Rathgar, Dublin 6.
Tel 903501
Seating 70
Open 6.30pm-8.30pm Tues-Sat; 11.30am - 3.30pm Sun
Average £13; £14.50 Fri/Sat set price table d'hote; house wine £9.50
Payment all major credit cards; EC, TC, LV.
International pub restaurant situated in a busy Dublin suburb. Up-market French bistro decor with wine racks around the room. Discreet lighting boosted by a candle on each table. Fish and chips are served in the Financial Times! The restaurant also boasts the most expensive burger in the world at £42.70 but the price does include a bottle of champagne! Well worth a visit! Specialities are sizzling spareribs, blackened chicken. Vegetarian available.
Babies/children allowed, child portions and menu, with under six free at Sunday lunch; high chairs. No smoking area (20). Not wheelchair friendly. Booking advisable weekends and Sunday lunch. Private room for parties.

Gallager's Restaurant and Pizzeria
83 Middle Abbey Street, Dublin 1
Tel 8729861
Seating 105
Open noon-midnight Sun-Thurs; noon-1pm Fri-Sat
Average £13; £5.25 lunch special; house wine £8.45, glass £1.80.
Payment all major credit cards; EC, TC, LV
Gallagers is not only ideally situated for busy shoppers in O'Connell Street, it is also an eating place for Abbey/Peacock theatregoers, and a short skip across the Ha'penny Bridge to the Olympia. The menu is varied but they pride themselves on their steaks. A hearty appetite will appreciate a 16oz sirloin for £9.95 while the lunch menu at £4.25 offers a fine selection. Beef strogonoff is served with chips while rice and vegetables come in a side dish. The service is quick, ideal for those rushing back to work. The decor is pleasant enough, whilst the black and white photographs of local celebrities provide an interesting distraction for the lone luncher or arrest the gaze in those gaps between conversations. Verdict: not extraordinary, but they are trying .
Babies/children catered for, child portions and menu; high chairs. No smoking area (62). Bookings advisable on special occasions. Pizza takeaway by arrangement.

McGrattan's
76 Fitzwilliam Lane, Dublin 2
Tel 6618808
Seating 120
Open 6pm-11pm, noon-2.45pm Mon-Fre; 6pm-12.30pm Mon-Thurs; 6pm-1.30am Fri/Sat.
Average £17 three courses; £12.95 set lunch; £9.95 Sunday lunch; house wine £10.95. Fully Licensed.
Payment all major credit cards; EC, TC.
12 ½% service.
Yet another restaurant neatly obscured off Lower Baggot Street (this time in Fitzwilliam Lane down past the Sunday Tribune offices), McGrattan's benefits from a very central location. The menu is Irish/French, tables are fairly well-spaced and napery is finer here than in some other restaurants in this section. Recently appointed inside, the

ceilings vault upwards to a central skylight. Parking round lunchtime is often a problem. The speciality is paupiette de saumon Marguerite and vegetarian dishes are available on request.
Babies/children catered for, child portions and menu on request; high chairs and baby changing room. No smoking area (20). Booking advisable. Tables outdoors (stables). Private room for parties. Takeaway by arrangement. Neat casual dress. Ground floor.

Sayers Restaurant
102-104 Terenure Road North, Dublin 6w
Tel 905986
Seating 120
Open 5pm-11.30pm Mon-Sat; 12.30pm-midnight Sun
Average £12; house wine £7.85.
Payment all major credit cards except DC; EC, TC, LV.
This sandy-coloured family restaurant with a distinctive candy-stripe awning is situated beside a funeral home but its comfortable interior quickly dispels any misgivings! The menu is wide-ranging and includes starters like breaded mussels and prawn cocktail, attractively presented in a scallop shell while smoked pasta - pasta with a creamy sauce featuring smoked salmon and chicken - is delicious. For dessert, banoffi is a speciality so if you don't know what that is, go to Sayers and find out. It will be worth it! A piano provides entertainment at weekends only.
Babies/children catered for, child portions and menu; high chairs. No smoking area (50). Booking advisable. Ground floor.

Trotters Restaurant
9 Fairview Strand, Fairview, Dublin 3
Tel 333681
Open 12.30pm-4pm Mon-Fri; 12.30pm-2am Sunday; 6pm-2am Mon-Sat
Average £13.50; £4.95 lunch; £6.90 early bird 6pm-7.30pm; house wine £8.80.
Payment all major credit cards; EC, TC, LV.
12 ½% service à la carte only.
As Fairview is rather starved of restaurants, Trotters is a bit of an oasis. It is really two restaurants - downstairs where lunch is served and a fancier upstairs for dinner. A main course like fried plaice or gammon in cider sauce with vegetables and potatoes is about £4.50 and the early bird menu at £6.95 includes dessert and coffee/tea.
Babies/children catered for, child portions and menu; high chairs and baby changing room. Wheelchair friendly (except toilets). No smoking area (25). Booking advisable. Takeaway by arrangement. Ground floor (lunch only). Stairs.

Spawell Lounge
Spawell Centre, Templeogue, Dublin 6w
Tel 901826
Seating 200
Open 12.30pm-2.30pm seven days; 7pm-10pm. limited à la carte.
Average £4.50-£5.50 lunch; house wine £8. Fully licensed.
Payment A, V; EC, TC, LV.
Anyone can avail of the par three golf course, driving range and other sports facilities at the Spawell Complex in

Templeogue. The restaurant is family-oriented so all age groups are catered for. The reasonably priced lunchtime carvery is extremely popular. Specialities are steak and seafood. Vegetarian available.
Babies/children catered for, child portions and menu; high chairs, baby changing room. No smoking area (20). Private room for parties. Neat casual dress. Ground floor.

Courtyard Restaurant
Belmont Court, Belmont Avenue, Dublin 4
Tel 2838815
Seating 150
Open noon-3pm, 5pm-midnight Mon-Sat; noon-3.30pm, 5pm-11pm Sun
Average £13; £5.95 carvery lunch; £4.95 main course and coffee; £7.95 early bird 5pm-7pm; £8.50 table d'hote Sunday lunch; house wine £7.95. Fully licensed.
Payment A, V; EC, TC, LV.
An informal restaurant situated just off Donnybrook's main street, convenient to Kielys and Madigans pubs. It specialises in good food at a reasonable price. Try to get a table in the glassed-in conservatory area at the far end of the restaurant which is light and airy. As for the food, the choice is extensive and the minute steak Diane is particularly nice.
Babies/children catered for, child portions and menu; baby changing room. No smoking area (32). Tables outdoors. Takeaway. Ground floor.

Dillons Deli Restaurant
21 Suffolk Street, Dublin 2
Tel 6774804/6774310
Seating 110
Open 8am-midnight seven days
Average £10; £4.95 special lunch; £7.70 house wine, ½ bottle £4.40, glass £1.95. Fully licensed.
Payment all major credit cards except DC; EC, TC.
Dillons can best be described as a family restaurant even though it has recently increased its scope by changing its name (now 'Deli' as well) and adding a deli counter just inside the door. It is something from the seventies making its concession to the nineties. House wine is Piat D'Or. Many hungry shoppers with bags from Clery's and Switzers sip tea and coffee on their break. It specialises in Irish stew and corned beef and cabbage; brown bread is homemade on the premises. Waitresses won't be wearing figure-hugging white leggings and decor will be neither a morass of colour nor minimalist.
Babies/children catered for, child portions, child menu - crayons provided; high chairs, baby changing room. No smoking area (55). Booking advisable. Private room for up to 24. Ground floor. Stairs to toilets.

Brahms and Liszt Restaurant
Old Airport Road, Santry, Dublin 9
Tel 8428383
Seating 80
Open noon-11pm seven days
Average £12; £4.50 lunch; £13.95 table d'hote dinner; £8.95 Sunday lunch; house wine litre £9.90. Fully licensed.
Payment all major credit cards; EC, TC LV.
This restaurant, redolent of Cockney rhyming slang, is in the old army barracks built in 1869, to keep the old north road free of highwaymen and other undesirable elements. Conveniently located beside the old airport road, the present operation is divided into three sections, giving an air of privacy. The menu is long and varied and prices are very middle-of-the-road. Interestingly enough, they home-smoke their own chicken and ribs, enough to make the restaurant worth a visit. As well as smoked ribs and chicken, specialities include pasta, grills and steaks. Vegetarian available.
Babies/children catered for, child portions and menu; high chairs and baby changing room. No smoking area (15). Booking advisable. Private room for parties. Ground floor. Stairs.

Stirrups Restaurant
The Goat
Goatstown House, Goatstown, Dublin 14
Tel 2984145
Seating 100
Open 12 noon-3pm; 6pm-11pm seven days
Average £14; £12.95 lunch; house wine £8.95.
Payment all major credit cards; EC, TC.
One of the oldest licensed premises in South Dublin, having celebrated 250 years of existence in 1992. The Sporting Pub emporium pays homage to every county, sport and notable achievement in Irish sporting life. Racing legends Arkle, Red Rum, Mill House, Dawn Run and Desert Orchid are all commemorated in Stirrups Restaurant which specialises in fish. The elevated piano is also an interesting feature. Specialities are beef and fresh lobster.
Babies/children catered for, child portions and menu; high chairs and baby changing room. No smoking area (16) Booking advisable. Function room for 200. Tables outdoors. Takeaway by arrangement. Ground floor

Pronto Grill
65 Ranelagh, Dublin 6
Tel 974174
Seating 40
Open 9am-midnight Sun-Thurs; 9am-1am Fri/Sat.
Average £6; £1.98 breakfast; £3.80 lunch; £7.90 dinner; house wine £5.90.
Payment TC, LV.
Don't expect crystal glass and starched linen tablecloths, you come here for exceptional value for money. For the evening special, there is smoked salmon mayonnaise, followed by sirloin steak and black forest gateau for dessert. Forego the starter and have a glass of wine or sherry instead. For a more special occasion, two can dine off the same menu, a bottle of house wine included for £11 each.
Babies/children catered for. No smoking area (26).Takeaway. Private room for parties. Ground floor.

Flanagans Restaurant
61 Upper O'Connell Street, Dublin 1
Tel 8731388
Seating 100
Open 8am-11.45pm seven days
Average £10 minimum lunch and dinner; house wine £7.65
Payment all major credit cards except AmEx; TC.
Steak house restaurant in central location offers a full breakfast at £2.75, and a lunchtime bistro menu, with smaller portions from the à la carte menu, at the £3.40 mark. It is a steak house which features in the Tom Clancy thriller 'Patriot Games'. If Clancy praises the food and service, then it is good enough for me. A popular tourist haunt in the heart of O'Connell Street. Speciality is 14oz sirloin steak.
Babies/children catered for; high chairs and baby changing room. Booking essential for six or more. Ground floor. Stairs.

Boss Crokers
38 Arran Quay, Dublin 7
Tel 8722400
Seating 250
Open noon-3pm; 7pm-10.30pm upstairs (100 seats); bar food all day.
Average £12-14 evening three courses including tea/coffee; £12.95 set price four/five courses; house wine £6.95. Fully licensed.
Payment all major credit cards; TC, LV.
Steak house restaurant. Decor - red/white small check tablecloths. Racing/pub eating house. Very long bar. Free entrance to nightclub on Fri/ Sat evenings for diners. Jazz brunch 12pm-3pm Sunday. Live music Sat - soul, blues, three girl band.
Specialities are steaks, fish, carvery. Vegetarian on request.
Babies/children allowed up to 7pm, child portions; baby changing facilities. No smoking area (30). Booking advisable. Tables outdoors. Private parties catered for 30-100. Takeaway sandwiches by arrangement. Ground floor. Stairs.

Silver Service Restaurant
Red Cow Inn, Naas Road, Clondalkin, Dublin 22
Tel 593650
Seating 120
Open 12.30pm-3pm, 6pm-10pm Mon-Fri; 12.30pm-10.30pm Sat/Sun
Average £12; £8.95 set lunch; £12.50 dinner Mon-Thurs; £15.50 Fri-Sun; £8.95 Sunday lunch. House wine £8.90. Fully licensed.
Payment all major credit cards except DC; EC, TC. Service charge included.
The Red Cow Inn is best described as an entertainment complex - downstairs in the public and lounge bars, a carvery lunch is served up to 3.30pm and bar food until 10.30pm. There is also live music and karaoke five nights. In the Silver Service Restaurant, the extensive menu includes a combination of steak, salmon and prawns. After dinner, there is a nightclub for dancing away the rest of the night. Cocktails are also served. Speciality is Red Cow steak. Vegetarian available.
Babies/children catered for, child portions and menu; high chairs and baby changing room. Not wheelchair friendly. No smoking area (40). Booking advisable weekends. Private room for parties. Neat casual dress. Stairs.

Cavern Restaurant
18 Suffolk Street, Dublin 2
Tel 6779918
Seating 70
Open 11am-11pm Mon-Sat; 11am-8pm Sun
Average £8.50; £1.50 breakfast all day; £8 house wine.
Payment A, V; EC, TC, LV
The concept for this restaurant is a diner/wine bar where musicians are encouraged to try out for a free meal and if they show any promise, are invited to play at weekends. With white-washed walls, benches and black tables and lots of posters, it promises to be fun and deserves to succeed. The extensive menu features burgers, omelettes, grills and steaks as well as cakes and pastries. Prices, particularly during the day are 'studenty' , encouraging a rather mixed clientele.
Babies/children catered for, child portions and menu; baby changing room. Not wheelcahir friendly. No smoking area (10). Takeaway. Stairs.

FXB's
1a Lower Pembroke Street, Dublin 2
Tel 6764606
Seating 100
Open 12.30pm-2.30pm Mon-Fri; 5.30pm-11.30pm Mon-Sat; closed Sun
Average £15; £10.95 lunch; £16.50 dinner; house wine £9.50. Fully licensed.
Payment all major credit cards; EC, TC, LV
This restaurant was the perfect diversification idea for Buckleys, the renowned Dublin butcher. Its reputation, which comes as no surprise, is founded on its quality meats, particularly its steaks. Off the courtyard entrance is a small brightly lit waiting area where you can enjoy a drink while perusing the menu. The main decision here is the size of your steak and the garnish, rather than whether you'll have meat or not! Steaks are cooked to taste so there tends to be a wait of 10-15 minutes. A large peppered steak with baked potato or French fries and a side order of fresh vegetables (extra for these) is a perfect meal. A comprehensive wine list will suit most tastes and budgets while lasagne and scampi are among alternatives on the menu. There is little choice for vegetarians but that's no surprise considering.
Babies/children catered for, child portions. No smoking area (30). Booking advisable. Tables outdoors. Private room for parties. Ground floor. Stairs to toilets and additional seating.

Clarke's Restaurant
24 Omni Park Shopping Centre, Swords Road, Dublin 9
Tel 8426266
Seating 180
Open 8am-midnight Mon-Sat; noon-midnight Sun
Average £10; £4 minimum from 4pm; £2.25 breakfast; £2.15 carvery lunch; house wine £7.75. Fully licensed.
Payment A, V; EC, TC, LV.

10% service a la carte only

One of the few restaurants in the Santry area, Clarke's has as its centrepiece an atrium with a garden full of indoor plants clustered around it. Brasserie style it is open from breakfast to midnight with a varied menu offering dishes from China and Italy with a large selection of chicken/steak choices. As it is family oriented, a mid-week cinema offer for £9.50 includes a ticket to any of the Omni-plex cinemas plus a two course dinner and coffee/tea, or for £14.95 you can enjoy a five course dinner with a main course of steak. As another option, complimentary bottle of Jacobs Creek is offered to a couple choosing from the appropriate menu. The restaurant is known for its Guinness and offers a full selection of cocktails. There is also a special rate for corporate lunches and rooms are available for meetings.

Babies/children catered for, child portions and menu; high chairs. No smoking area (20). Booking advisable. Private room for parties. Neat casual dress. Ground floor. Stairs.

Joel's Restaurant

Newlands Cross, Naas Road, Dublin 22
Tel 592968/594510
Seating 150
Open 8am-11.30pm Mon-Sat; 9am-10pm Sun
Average £11; £4.25 minimum; £3.50 breakfast 8am-noon; £4.75 carvery lunch Mon-Fri; £8.70 Sunday lunch; house wine £6.95. Fully licensed. Payment all major credit cards; EC, TC.

Joel's is located at the busy intersection of the Naas dual carriageway. The restaurant designed to an American concept features a conservatory near the main entrance where you can enjoy a pre-dinner drink and a series of booths to the left of the dining area afford privacy for business meetings or a quiet dinner à deux. The extensive menu emphasises grills, poultry and steaks but also includes seafood, omelettes and vegetarian options and prices are quite reasonable.

Babies/children catered for, child portions and menu; high chairs and baby changing room. No smoking area (22). Neat casual dress. Ground floor.

Out of Town

In times gone by, eateries outside the city centre existed either as an excuse for late night drinking - beyond the long arm of the law - or to facilitate illicit liaisons - beyond the long arms of an irate spouse. Today the combined forces of drink-driving laws, expanded suburbia and a more relaxed approach to casual dining out have encouraged the mushrooming of restaurant options away from downtown Dublin.

Choices range from ginghamed cheap and cheerful to seriously trendy wine-bars and earnest small restaurants where many a neophyte star chef is quietly earning his wings. In addition to being adjacent to where Dubliners live and play at night, out-of-towners frequently have the added attraction of unique settings like the Wicklow Arms on its pretty village hillside and the antique-studded Beaufield Mews (see "Curiosities") with its old walled gardens that have provided the backdrop for several generations of bridal photographs.

A recent phenomenon not to be ignored is the publicans' reaction to declining drink sales, with tempting bar food, often of cordon bleu standard from eager young acolytes of the Ballymaloe or Alix Gardner schools. The Purty Kitchen's (see "Seafood") seafood chowder and brown bread set standards Dublin hotel chefs would do well to emulate.

de Selby's

17 Patrick Street, Dun Laoghaire, Co Dublin
Tel 2841761
Seating 120 + 60 outside
Open 5.30pm-11pm Mon-Sat; noon-6pm Sun; 12.30pm-2.30pm May-Sept
Average £14; house wine £9.
Payment all major credit cards; EC, TC, LV

de Selby is the eponymous Flann O'Brien character, a self-styled philosopher of the novel "The Third Policeman" who, fiction would have it, was a local of Dun Laoghaire. There is no portrait of de Selby save for the interpretation on the window of this roomy restaurant. Fitting, therefore, that the place should double as an art gallery where the exhibits of struggling, local artists are bought and sold from the walls as slowly as you can say "Out Back". The "Out Back" is the great outdoor reconstruction of a 1940s Irish village [complete with unvandalised telephone and road signs pointing vaguely in the right direction (how times change!)]. The food is for a family night out: excellent burgers and steaks, creamy pasta dishes and chicken every way. Starters include lobster salad, warm goats' cheese salad with walnut dressing and garlic mushrooms. Children are welcome and the staff are quick with the high chairs, bibs and immediate plates of chips and bowls of ice cream. The "Out Back" restaurant menu boasts roast quail with bread sauce and game chips for £9.25, traditional Irish stew (as de Selby says, 'it's your only man') for £6.95 as well as a vegetarian section.

Babies/children catered for, child portions and menu; high chairs and emergency nappies. No smoking area (50). Booking advisable. Tables outdoors with 60 seats. Ground floor. Stairs to toilets.

Greens Restaurant

Leopardstown Inn, Brewery Road, Blackrock, Co Dublin
Tel 2889189
Seating 80
Open 5.30pm-11pm Mon-Sat; 12.30pm-3pm Sunday lunch
Average £15; £7.75 early bird; house wine £8.50. Fully licensed.
Payment all major credit cards; EC, TC.

Modern cuisine restaurant specialising in seafood while accommodating the vegetarian palate. Recently re-opened after a fire last year, this restaurant boasts an unusual revamped interior with numerous features including a reproduction of an ancient Italian fresco - a must for all interior design enthusiasts.

Babies/children catered for; high chairs. Not wheelchair friendly. No smoking area (14). Booking advisable. Private room for parties. Ground floor. Stairs.

Duggans Bistro
43 Temple Road, Blackrock, Co Dublin
Tel 2884998
Seating 30, excluding garden
Open 7.30am-7.30pm Mon-Fri; 9.30am-7.30pm Sat/Sun
Average £3.95; £1.95 full breakfast including juice; house wine £7, glass £1.50
Payment EC,TC, LV
A find! A reasonably priced French restaurant run by a most amiable proprietress who combines a continental atmosphere with good food. There is even a secluded wine garden, complete with fountain. An idyllic venue, but unfortunately not open for dinner.
Babies/children catered for, child portions. Not really wheelchair friendly. No smoking area (10). Booking advisable evening. Tables outdoors in the wine garden. Private rooms for parties. Takeaway. Upstairs.

Daniel's Restaurant
34a, Glasthule Road, Sandycove, Co Dublin
Tel 2841027
Seating 40
Open 6pm-midnight Tues-Sun
Average £16.95; £6 chef's specials; house wine £9.25.
Payment all major credit cards; EC, TC.
A small upstairs restaurant on the Dalkey side of Sandycove, tucked away off the Glasthule Road. This restaurant deserves to be better known for its creamy prawn bisque with wonderfully subtle flavours. The chicken fricassée is different and good value at £7.95. Fussy decor aside, be assured of cuisine that is a quantum leap away from nouvelle. Specialities are guinea fowl, roast crispy duck and fish. Vegetarian available.
Babies/children catered for, child portions; high chairs. Not wheelchair friendly. No smoking area (20). Booking advisable at weekends. Stairs.

Bistro Vino
56 Glasthule Road, Sandycove, Co Dublin
Tel 2806097/2845746
Seating 50
Open 5pm-11.30pm seven nights
Average £14; £9.75 early bird 7pm-9pm; house wine £8.50
Payment A, V; EC.
Popular with more dedicated gourmets who come for relatively hearty continental fare in a bistro atmosphere at reasonable prices. Pictures reflect the taste in music - blues and jazz. For the alternatives, there is 'designer' pasta, pigeon farcita - "strips of marinated wood pigeon pan-fried, served in a rich game sauce with tagliatelle, crispy bacon and pinenuts", complete with a green salad and garlic bread - all for only £7.95.
Specialities are lobster and crab.
Not wheelchair friendly. No smoking area (12). Booking advisable weekends. Takeaway by arrangement.

Floyds Restaurant
Marine Parade, Sandycove, Co Dublin.
Tel 2845141
Seating 42
Open 6pm-11pm Tues-Sat; 1pm-3pm Sun
Average £17; £11.95 minimum Sunday lunch house wine £9.25. Fully licensed.
Payment A.V; EC, TC. 10% service for over ten.
Formerly the Mirabeau, and more recently La Vie en Rose, this restaurant with a Florentine decor boasts a warm atmosphere and friendly service as well as a view across Dublin Bay. Specialities are fish and chicken and prawn Vegetarian available.
Babies/children catered for, child menu. No smoking area (12). Booking advisable. Tables outdoors. Takeaway by arrangement. Private room for parties. Ground floor.

South Bank Restaurant
1 Martello Terrace, Seafront, Dun Laoghaire, Co Dublin
Tel 2808788
Seating 50
Opening 7pm-10.30pm Mon-Sat; closed Sun
Average £17; house wine £9, glass £2

Payment all major credit cards; EC, TC

This restaurant is run by the proprietor, David Byrne and his wife, who ensure personal service and maintain consistent standards. Soft lighting and an array of mixed art create a unique atmosphere. On Bloomsday (June 16) to commemorate Leopold Bloom's historic walk around Dublin, and since this amble originated in Sandycove, the South Bank has become the traditional breakfast stop-off.

Babies/children allowed. Not really wheelchair friendly. No smoking area (5), Booking advisable. Tables outdoors. Ground floor. Two steps.

Odells Restaurant

49 Sandycove Road, Dun Laoghaire, Co Dublin
Tel 2842188
Seating 34
Open 6.30pm-10.30pm Tues-Sun; closed Mon
Average £16; house wine £9.50. Fully licensed.
Payment all major credit cards; EC, TC.
10% service.

Attractive intimate upstairs restaurant with plenty of tables for two. Imaginative food at relatively moderate prices, ranges from French and Italian to Thai and Irish in the form of fresh crab and lobster from nearby Bulloch Harbour. Fillet of beef, pork and lamb are smothered in rich sauces and, if you still have room, chocolate mousse cake is sinful. Specialities are fresh fish and lamb and there is also a vegetarian platter.

Not wheelchair friendly. Booking advisable, essential at weekends. First floor. Stairs.

Wishbone Restaurant

Eagle House, 18-20 Glasthule Road, Glasthule, Co Dublin
Tel 2808021
Seating 90
Open 5.30pm-11pm Mon-Fri; 12.30-11pm Sat; 11am (brunch)-10pm Sun
Average £10, £5 minimum all day; house wine £8.25. Fully licensed
Payment all major credit cards; EC, TC, LV

A family restaurant whose menu emphasises healthy eating. An adjoining wine bar serves canapes on Fri/Sat from 10pm-3am. There is even a magician to provide children's entertainment.

Babies/children catered for, child portions and menu; high chairs and baby changing room. Not wheelchair friendly. No smoking area (40). Private parties catered for. First floor. Stairs.

Trudi's Restaurant

107 Lower George's Street, Dun Laoghaire, Co Dublin
Tel:2805318
Seating 55
Open 7.30pm-11pm Tues-Sat.
Average £15-17; à la carte only; house wine £8.50.
Payment all major credit cards; EC, TC.

Galleried ground floor bistro. One of the longest-running success stories of this genre, Trudi's has a timeless atmosphere. A cosy bar downstairs is an obligatory pre-dinner stop; some have been known to forego the pleasures of the dining area upstairs in its favour. One has a feeling, however, from the declining exterior that Roly's attention lies more with his current love than this old

flame.
Vegetarian available.
No smoking area (3). Booking advisable.

Wicklow Arms
Delgany, Co Wicklow
Tel 2874611
Seating 52
Open 7pm-10pm Tues-Sat; 1.30pm-10pm Sun bar food
Payment all major credit cards; EC, TC, LV.
Lounge bar restaurant, a mere 20 minutes away from Dublin city centre, in the beautiful village of Delgany beside the Wicklow mountains, this family-run business is operated as a restaurant rather than a pub. Its à la carte menu encompasses international, European and pub grub as well as a table d'hôte with different specials each week. Droves of people make the pilgrimage and weekends are especially packed. Garlic mushrooms are a great favourite and there is a limited cocktail menu.
Not wheelchair friendly. Booking advisable, essential at weekends. Air conditioned function room. Private room for parties. Ground floor.

Mountain View House
Stepaside, Co. Dublin
Tel 2954232
Seating 120
Open 10.30am-11.20pm Mon-Sat; 4pm-10pm Sun
Average £11; £2 minimum; house wine £8. Fully licensed.
Payment TC
This popular restaurant boasts the best pepper sauce in Dublin. Its varied menu includes 14/16oz t-bone steak at £9 which includes chips, coleslaw or jacket potato and vegetarians are catered for by arrangement. There is live entertainment in the form of traditional music at weekends.
Babies/children allowed up to 8pm. Not wheelchair friendly. Booking advisable. Private room for parties. Catering menu. Ground floor. Pitch & putt in back £1.30 + 50p ball.

Lavin's Thatched Restaurant
The Hill, Stillorgan, Co Dublin
Tel 2883026
Seating 45
Open 6.30pm-11pm Mon-Sat; 12.30pm-3pm Sunday lunch
Average £19; £18.95 table d'hôte; house wine £9.50. Fully licensed.
Payment all major credit cards; EC, TC.
10% service.
Bewleys award-winning restaurant attached to the Stillorgan Orchard Pub, reputed to be the largest thatched building in Ireland. With a central fireplace, it has gone back to the old style, yet is still small enough to allow for personal service. A list of over 100 wines gives the connoisseur something to mull over and even the restrooms are worth a mention for their complementary supply of toiletries. Its olde worlde charm makes Lavins somewhere special for that extra special night out, enhanced by background classical piano music. While the menu is comprehensive and everything is cooked to the chef's specifications, Lavin's will cater for any particular preference. Their flambéd dishes are very popular and vegetarian options are always available.
Babies/children allowed. Not wheelchair friendly. No smoking area (10). Booking advisable weekdays, essential at weekends. Private room for parties. Presentable dress. Ground floor.

Pepper Cannister Restaurant
Mill House, Lower Kilmacud Road, Stillorgan, Co Dublin
Tel 2886206
Seating 120
Open 6pm-11pm Mon-Sat; 12.30pm-3pm, 5pm-9pm Sun
Average £12; house wine £8.95. Fully licensed
Payment all major credit cards; EC, TC, LV
This is an international restaurant which prides itself on value for money and its steaks. A middle-of-the-road establishment, it caters very much for families.
Babies/children catered for, child portions and menu; high chairs and baby changing room. No smoking area (16). Booking advisable. Stairs.

Partners Restaurant
*Unit 13 Rathfarnham Shopping Centre,
Dublin 14
Tel 931372
Seating100
Open 9am-6pm Sat-Wed; 9am-7.30pm Thur/Fri.
Average £6-£6.50; house wine £6.95, ¼ bottle
£2.20
Payment LV*
Partners is a self-service cafe with a decor reminiscent of the very early eightie when suburban shopping-centres first started to appear. According to manageress, Marie Holland, all the food is homemade, freshly prepared each day with two different hot lunches as well as the ever popular lasagne and quiche which, along with a vegetarian option, are always available. Desserts, especially cheesecake and meringues, go down a treat.
Babies/children catered for, child portions and menu; high chairs. Not wheelchair friendly. No smoking area (50). Takeaway. Stairs

Paddy Whacks
*26 Castle Street, Dalkey, Co Dublin
Tel none
Seating 100
Open 5pm-11pm Mon-Fri; 9am-10pm Sat/Sun
Average £12; house wine £7.95. Fully licensed.
Payment all major credit cards; EC
Babies/children catered for, child portions and menu; high chairs. Booking advisable at weekends. Private room for parties. Takeaway. Ground floor. Stairs.*

Cooper's Restaurant
*The Golden Ball, Enniskerry Road, Kilternan, Co Dublin
Tel 2959349
Seating 75
Open 5.30pm-midnight Mon-Sat; 1pm-4pm, 5pm-10.30pm Sun; 11am-11pm bar menu seven days.
Average £15; £12.95/13.95 set meals; £10.95/12.95 Sunday lunch; house wine £8.50.
Fully licensed
Payment A, V; EC, TC, LV.*

Service charge for over ten.

Another of the large, floppy, laminated menu brigade and sister restaurant of Coopers, Monkstown, this restaurant is linked with the Golden Ball pub. Starters range from soup (£1.80), (gazpacho (£1.95) also served), to avocado and seafood cocktail (£2.95). The menu is across-the-board to snare any taste: fowl, fish, sausages and steak ... a prop-me-up if you're returning (with family) from a roam in the country.

Babies/children catered for, ½ price child portions and menu; high chairs. No smoking area (by arrangement). Booking advisable. Tables outdoors. Private room for parties. Ground floor.

Curtlestown House Country Restaurant

Curtlestown, Enniskerry, Co Wicklow
Tel 2825083
Seating 45
Open 8pm-10.30pm Tues-Sat; 12.45pm-2pm Sunday lunch
Average £17; £10 lunch; house wine £10
Payment A, V; EC, TC

Essentially a farmhouse with sub-divided rooms, Curtlestown House is never short of traffic - limited capacity and large demand see to that. Not that the food doesn't account for this, the hard-working chef ensures it does and with some success. A popular venue for large parties (and well used by inhabitants of the area) who might occupy a room to themselves, service is sometimes stretched when this happens and you may try an extra aperitif while the restaurant tries your patience. The menu is mainly Irish salmon, lamb, chicken, steaks - but with occasional foreign input (gravlax). The cost of food is reasonable considering the care, quality and presentation where one of the chief attractions is the magnificent view over the Glencree valley while sipping your chosen beverage on fine days (remember them?)

Babies/children allowed under strict supervision, ½ portions Sunday lunch only. Not wheelchair friendly. No smoking area. Booking advisable, essential at weekends and during summer. Private room for parties. Grond floor.

Breakers Restaurant

1 New Street, Malahide, Co Dublin
Tel 8452584
Seating 90
Open 5.30pm-midnight Mon-Sat; 12.30pm-11pm Sun and bank hol Mon.
Average £13; £9.95 main course special; £8.95 table d'hôte Sunday lunch; house wine £8.95.
Fully licensed.
Payment A, V; EC, LV.

This brasserie-style restaurant with a distinctive nautical atmosphere is a favourite with visitors. Specialising in steak and seafood, provision is also made for vegetarians. For entertainment, there is live music every Tuesday.

Babies/children catered for, child portions and menu; high chairs and baby changing room. No smoking area (18). Booking advisable at weekends. Ground floor.

The Buttery
6 Church Road, Malahide, Co Dublin
Tel 8450095
Seating100
Open 10am-11pm seven days
Average £15 four courses; £5.50 two course lunch; breakfast from £1.99; house wine £8.95.
Payment all major credit cards.

This brasserie style restaurant distinguishes itself by its two house specialities - steaks and fettucine. While catering for vegetarians, a tourist menu features favourites like Irish stew, coddle or bacon and cabbage. Its appeal is further enhanced by traditional music sessions on Wednesday to Saturday, and a patio bordered with flower beds and decorated with hanging pots is ideal for al fresco dining, weather permitting!

Babies/children catered for; high chairs and baby changing room. No smoking area (20). Booking advisable in the evening. Private room for parties. Takeaway. Ground floor.

Old Street Wine Bar
Old Street, Malahide, Co Dublin
Tel 8451882
Seating 14
Open noon-3pm, 6pm-11pm seven days.
Average under £5; £4.50 full Irish brunch weekends and bank holidays, including glass of bucks fizz; house wine £8.95, glass £1.85.
Payment all major credit cards except DC; EC, TC.

An intimate wine bar has both an open fire and a patio, thus accommodating dining all year round. Specialising in home cooked food, the limited menu includes vegetarian options. Queen of puddings appears on the sweet selection, as well as Victorian delights that some of us have forgotten and others have never known. However this is a wine bar. Enjoy a bottle of wine and nibble from a selection of Irish farmhouse cheeses as you drink.

Babies and children tolerated. Wheelchair friendly (except toilets). No smoking area (4). Tables outdoors. Ground floor.

Dee Gee's
opposite DART Station, Howth, Co Dublin
Tel 392641
Seating 42
Open 8am-11.30pm seven days
Average £10; £2.95 breakfast till noon; house wine £8.50.
Payment A, V; EC, TC.
Howth's eating and meeting place with an open plan kitchen where a cross section of the community can enjoy good quality food and wine in unpretentious surroundings. Those who come in for a glass of wine or a cup of coffee are no less welcome than others who have a full meal. The menu caters for all tastes ranging from fish and steak to Italian. Nor have vegetarians been forgotten.
Babies/children catered for, child portions and menu; baby changing room. No smoking area (12). Booking advisable at weekends. Tables outdoors. Ground floor.

Malahide Castle Restaurant
Malahide, Co Dublin
Tel 8452940
Talbot Room Restaurant/coffee shop
Seating 40/50-60
12.30pm-3pm restaurant; 10am-5pm coffee shop Mon-Fri; 11am-6pm Sat/Sun.
Average £15; £11.25 Sunday lunch; house wine £8.95. Fully licensed.
Payment all major credit cards; EC, TC.
Malahide Castle which stands on 25 acres of ground, dates back to 1185 and was the home of the Talbot family until 1978. Rose Talbot, the sole surviving family member, now lives in Tasmania and makes an annual visit to the family home, which is now maintained by Dublin County Council. The restaurant and coffee shop located on the ground floor are run by Mary O'Callaghan. The Talbot Room, the upmarket end of the operation, provides a genteel setting enhanced by an interesting menu specialising in Sunday lunches. It is a pity that such a spectacular restaurant is not open in the evenings. Lunch in the coffee shop for about £5 features Dover sole. Speciality is fish and vegetarians are catered for.
Babies/children catered for, child menu; high chairs and baby changing room. No smoking throughout. Booking advisable in restaurant. Neat casual dress. Takeaway.

Adrian's Restaurant
3 Abbey Street, Howth, Co Dublin,
Tel 391696
Seating 40
Open 12.30pm-3.30pm; 6.30pm-9.30pm Mon-Sat; 2pm-8pm Sun
Average £10; £16 table d'hôte dinner; house wine £9.50.
Payment all major credit cards; EC, TC
Adrian's is a busy little bistro whose inner maritime decor reflects its coastal location in Howth, a short drive north of the city centre. Food is prepared by Catriona Holden, an artistic young chef, whose family runs this cosy restaurant and her turn of hand adds credence to an interesting, creative menu assuring fresh ingredients carefully put together. There is an excellent selection of poached fish, pan-fried Barbary duck and a variety of pasta dishes, like pasta with duck and apple. It is noteworthy that the pasta, as well as the breads and soups, are all homemade. Blinis - buckwheat pancakes - are another treat. Dinner starts with crudités and a herb dip and ends with excellent dessert choices like chocolate mousse and Amaretto cheesecake. The wine list is short, moderately priced and well chosen.
Not wheelchair friendly. No smoking area (12). Booking advisable. Private room for parties. Takeaway by arrangement. Ground floor. Stairs.

Oscar Taylor's Restaurant
Coast Road, Malahide, Co Dublin
Tel 8450399
Seating 95
Open 5.30pm-11pm Mon-Sat; 12.30pm-10pm Sun
Average £12.50; house wine £7.55. Fully licensed.
Payment A, V; EC, TC, LV.
Located on the coast road out of Malahide opposite the beach, with partitioned booths and rather bright lighting setting the style,

this steak house is upstairs in the Stuart Hotel. Steaks and seafood rank as its specialities and vegetarian dishes are available on request.
Babies/children catered for; high chairs. Not wheelchair friendly. No smoking area.

Cassells Restaurant
Grove Hotel, Grove Road, Malahide, Co Dublin
Tel 8452208
Seating 100
Open 5.30pm-11pm Mon-Sat; -10pm Sun.
Average £13.50 including coffee.
Fully licensed.
Payment A, V; EC, TC.
Speciality - steaks. Vegetarian available.
Babies/children catered for, child portions and menu; high chairs and baby changing room. Wheelchair friendly (except toilets). No smoking area (20). Booking advisable. Private room for parties up to 60.

Food Fair Restaurant
Dublin Airport
Tel 8407466
Seating 500
Open 6am-9pm Mon-Thurs, -10pm Fri, -10.30pm Sat, -10pm Sun(summer); 6am-8pm Mon-Fri, -9pm Sat; -8pm Sun (winter)
Average £7; £2.50 minimum breakfast; £4.65 full breakfast including pot of tea/coffee, toast and butter; house wine £7.80, ½ bottle £4.95
Payment all major credit cards; EC, TC, LV
This self-service restaurant, located on the floor above Departures, will be familiar to most who have paid a visit to Dublin airport for whatever reason. Here the emphasis is on speedy and efficient service rather than imaginative cuisine but vegetarians are catered for. While prices are generally on a par with city centre eateries, the house wine is certainly below average.
Babies/children catered for, child portions and menu; high chairs and baby changing room. No smoking area (180). Stairs. Lift.

Silver Lining Restaurant
Dublin Airport
Tel 8407466
Seating 64
Opening noon-3pm seven days
Average £10; £6.95 quick lunch main course in 20 mins guaranteed or your money back; £7.75 for two courses; house wine £8.95. Fully licensed.
Payment all major credit cards; 12 ½% service.
This is the airport's flagship restaurant with full waiter service and all the trimmings. A window seat commands a view of the tarmac and all the goings on. The menu, which offers a good selection including vegetarian, changes bi-weekly.
Babies/children catered for, child portions and menu, high chairs and baby changing room. No smoking area (22). Booking advisable. Private room for parties. Escalators. Lift.

Le Chateau Restaurant
Swords, Co Dublin
Tel 8406533
Seating 70
Open 12.30pm-2.30pm Tues-Fri; 7pm-10.30pm Mon-Sat; earlier opening by arrangement; closed Sun.
Average £20; £10.50 lunch; £14.50 table d'hote dinner; house wine £8.75
Payment all major credit cards; EC, TC, LV
Although this restaurant is situated off the beaten track down a narrow alley opposite Cock Tavern, it has not hindered its winning a plethora of culinary awards. Delights include Pasta Tara - fresh pasta, garlic, baby mushrooms in a light cream sauce served with garlic bread. A main course could be baked breast of chicken with a potato herbed stuffing then wrapped in bacon to keep in the juices. To end, a luscious chocolate Amaretto gateau is a confection of meringue, light almond sponge, chocolate butter, cream and apricot purée all smothered in Amaretto. John Dowd, the proprietor, also runs a cookery school.
Babies/children catered for (not late at night); child portions and menu; high chairs and baby changing room. Not wheelchair friendly. No

smoking area (35). Booking advisable. Private room for parties. Takeaway by arrangement. Neat dress. Stairs.

The Old Schoolhouse Restaurant
Coolbanagher, Church Road, Swords, Co Dublin
Tel 8402846/8404160
Seating 55
Open12.30pm-2.30pm Mon-Fri; 6.30-10.30pm Mon-Sat; closed Sun and bank holidays
Average £19.50; £10.95 table d'hôte; £18.50 dinner; house wine £9.95.

This charming restaurant is a tastefully refurbished old schoolroom adjoining a spacious conservatory where potted plants, old pine, and dark reds and greens bestow an informal and pleasant aura. The Old Schoolhouse offers an inventive menu with quality traditional and home-cooked dishes, like smoked chicken and fresh duck terrine with red pepper sauce, sautéd calves' liver with bacon and fillet steak au poivre. The seafood, like the vegetables, is varied and creative. Entrées may be preceded or accompanied by homemade bread and soups. The wine list provides a broad range of prices and choices with monthly specials are a clever addition.

Babies/children catered for, child portions; baby changing room. Wheelchair friendly (except toilets). No smoking area (20). Booking advisable. Tables outdoors. Private room for parties. Ground floor. Stairs.

Robinhood House Restaurant
5 Robin Hood Road, Clondalkin, Dublin 22
Tel 503033
Seating 56
Open 8am-5pm Mon-Fri; 12.30pm-3.30pm Sun; closed Sat
Average £7; £2.85 breakfast; £7.50 Sunday lunch; house wine £6.95/£7.95.
Payment A, V; EC.

A prize is offered to those who can find this restaurant. The best approach is via the Long Mile Road, into the Robinhood industrial Estate, then follow the signs. A converted house, it is clean and rather fussy but few places in Dublin serve a three course meal for as little. While the cuisine may not be adventurous, the price is the thing and what's more, the house wine is good value too.

Babies/children catered for, child portions and menu; high chairs. No smoking area (16). Table outdoors. Takeaway. Ground floor.

Kingswood Country House and Restaurant
Old Kingswood, Naas Road, Clondalkin, Dublin 22
Tel 592428
Seating 45
Open 12.30pm-2.30pm Mon-Fri & Sun; 6.30pm-10.30pm Mon-Sat; closed Sunday dinner
Average £12.95 lunch; £18.95 dinner; house wine £9.50
Payment all major credit cards; EC, TC.
12 ½% service.

This countryhouse-cum-restaurant, convenient to the many industrial estates on the Long Mile and Naas Roads, is a pleasant surprise for those who take the trouble to go out this way for dinner. Standing in its own grounds just off the Naas dual carriageway, much of the produce used in the kitchen comes from its adjoining kitchen garden. The varied menu changes daily. A typical starter is a salad of smoked salmon, melon and avocado served with a lemon and honey dressing. Priding themselves on their traditional dishes, they make their own soda bread which is served with their special Irish stew, Kingswood style. Vegetarian dishes are available on request. (Not just a restaurant, there are also seven bedrooms and Kingswood also caters for business meetings and private parties).

Babies/children catered for, child portions at lunch and child menu Sunday lunch; high chairs. No smoking area (10). Booking advisable. Private room for parties. Neat casual dress. Ground floor.

The Colonnade
The Grand Hotel, Malahide, Co Dublin
Tel 8450633
Seating 120
Open 12.30pm-2.30pm, 6pm-10.15pm seven days.
Average £16.50; £16.60 set-price dinner; house wine £8.75.
12 ½% service charge.
Payment all major credit cards; EC, TC.

Like a lighthouse beacon on the North County Dublin coastline overlooking the sea in the stockbroker belt of Malahide, The Grand Hotel is both stylish and luxurious. The restaurant, The Colonnade, offers a substantial à la carte and table d'hôte menu with a heavy emphasis, as you'd expect, on seafood - escargots, smoked salmon and trout, scallops, salmon, monkfish and Dover sole. House specialities include beef and dishes range from £10.50-12.50. Vegetarians aren't neglected and three alternatives are offered at £6.95. Side orders are charged as extra and the house wine is favourably priced at £8.75.

Babies/children catered for, child's menu; high chairs. No smoking are (30). Semi-formal dress. Ground floor.

Meridian Restaurant
The Marine Hotel, Sutton, Dublin 13
Tel 322613
Seating 70
Open 12.30pm-2.30pm seven days; 6.30pm-10.15pm Tue-Sat, 6.30pm-10pm Sun.
Average £16.90 table d'hôte five course dinner; £10/10.50 lunch; house wine £9.75.
Payment all major credit cards; EC, TC.

Sister hotel of The Grand in Malahide, less grandiose and located at Sutton Cross, the speciality again is seafood. A buffet lunch is served outside the restaurant Monday-Freday for those not wishing to commit to a formal, fully-fledged sit-down meal.

Babies/children catered for, child menu; high chairs. No smoking area. Takeaway by arrangement. Neat dress. Ground floor.

Killakee House Restaurant

Killakee Road, Rathfarnham, Dublin 16

Tel 932645/917

Seating 50

Open 12.30pm-2.30pm Mon-Fri; 7pm-11pm Mon-Sat; closed Sun

Average £20-£25; £11.95-£19.95 five course dinner; house wine £8.95. Fully licensed.

Payment all major credit cards. 10% service dinner only

In the foothills of the Wicklow mountains overlooking the city, lies Killakee House, a robust 18th-century stone building with a small tower and a big history. Former residence of the Countess Markievicz and noted for a storm of psychic activity in the late sixties and early seventies, this hostel has certainly earned its right to display images of a black cat throughout. Although set in the bosom of the countryside, it services the local urban populations of Tallaght (ten minutes drive / four minutes from the motorway) and Rathfarnham. The menu features a large selection of seafood (av. £12 main course), meat and poultry similarly priced. Appetising starters range from peppered duck livers (£5.50), to smoked pigeon breast(£5.25) to baked egg with fettucine verdi(£5.25). The table d'hote menu is worth a particular glance for the five course dinner for as little as £11.25.

Babies/children catered for, child portions; high chairs. No smoking area. Booking advisable weekends. Tables outdoors. Private room for parties. Takeaway by arrangement. Ground floor. First floor restaurant and stairs.

Killakee House Restaurant

Killakee Road, Rathfarnham, Dublin 16.
Telephone 932645, 932917

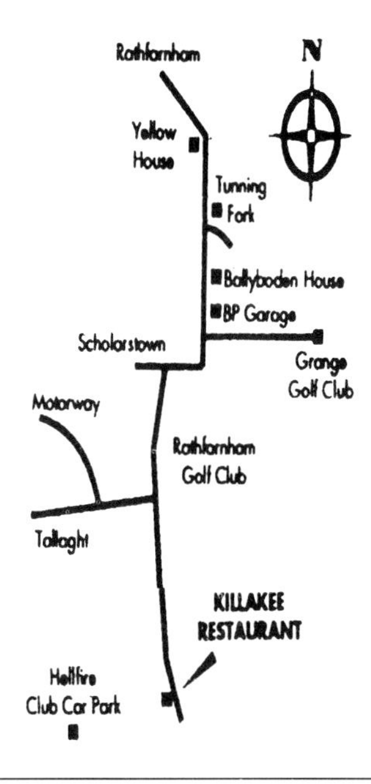

This is the all-sorts bag of restaurants - the sort of one-offs that have invented themselves as a category - coffee houses, creperies, caffs.

Wine bar with a difference is Mitchell's Cellars, genuinely the old cellars of Dublin's oldest family-owned wine merchants. In addition to familiar political faces who nip across from Dail Eireann, Mitchell's have their own alcove table where wine gurus from around the world are entertained.

The battily named Batz is hidden down a laneway and is still packed out by diners who equate the wonderful food with going home to granny's.

In a totally different slot is Jury's Coffee Dock which is closed only for an hour and a half out of every 24 and is the traditional ending of many a bleary debs' night.

Cafe Java

145 Upper Leeson Street, Dublin 4
Tel 6608775
Seating 28
Open 8am-6pm Mon-Fri; 9am-5pm Sat; 11am-5pm Sun
Average £3.75; £2.95 minimum 12.30pm-2pm; house wine £8.95, glass £1.95
Payment A. V; EC, TC

This is one of those little gems that could go completely unnoticed unless someone 'in-the-know' brought it to your attention. It's the ideal venue for a long leisurely breakfast/brunch over a full selection of newspapers or some good chat! A small narrow coffeeshop/lunchtime venue with a Mediterranean air, is brightly lit and has coloured masks hanging on the walls and an open glass area at the back that soaks in the sun. The menu warns that everything is prepared while you wait so bear this in mind - the relaxed, casual atmosphere certainly seems to have affected the staff! The food - when it does arrive - is well worth the wait: corn muffins, blueberry muffins; freshly squeezed orange juice, croissants, preserves .. then eggs: bacon, eggs and sausages; and any other combination you might think of.

Babies/children allowed. No smoking area (4). Tables outdoors. Takeaway. Ground floor.

Cafe Carolina

66 Dame Street, Dublin 2
Tel 6777378
Seating 25
Open 8am-10.30pm Mon-Thurs; 9am-4am Fri-Sat; 9am-1am Sun
Average £4. Unlicensed.
Payment A, V; EC, TC, LV

A small, cosy and rather trendy cafe/creperie close to the Olympia theatre so it attracts a Thespian clientele among others. A varied selection of food is offered at inexpensive prices and recently they have started to specialise in pancakes, both savoury and sweet. The choice is eclectic to say the least. The bacon, mushroom, spinach and garlic variety in a provençale sauce

(served with a salad) provides a filling meal for £2.50. Very affordable and very popular.
Babies/children catered for by arrangement. Wheelchair friendly (except toilets). No smoking area (7). Private room for parties. Takeaway. Ground floor.

Vertigo
40 South Richmond Street, Portobello, Dublin 8
Tel none
Seating 38
Open 10am-midnight Mon-Wed; 10am-4am Thurs-Fri; noon-4am Sat; noon-1am Sun
Average £7; £2.50 breakfast; house wine £7.95
Payment LV.
This place is quite unusual - for a start, they built it themselves for £4,000. David Trunk opened this restaurant to please himself. A regular haunt for the alternative set, coffee refills are free. Specialities are barbecued spareribs and breakfasts.
Vegetarian available.
Babies/children catered for, child portions and menu. Wheelchair friendly (except toilets). No smoking area (8). Ground floor. Stairs

Coffee Dock
Jury's Hotel, Ballsbridge, Dublin 4
Tel 6605000
Seating 87
Open 22 1/2 hours, closed 4.30am-6am seven days
Average £10; £6 set lunch; £9 dinner; house wine £10.50.
Payment all major credit cards; EC, TC, LV.
12 ½% service
This grill restaurant specialises in steaks, burgers, club sandwiches. and has vegetarian options.
Babies/children catered for, child menu; high chairs. No smoking area (27). Ground floor.

Batz
10 Baggot Lane, off Pembroke Road/Upper Baggot Street, Dublin 4
Tel 6600363
Seating 60
Open5 12.15pm-2.30pm Mon-Fri; closed Sat/Sun
Average £8;. house wine £8.25.
Payment all major credit cards; EC, TC
There was a long pause between the first time Batz was recommended me and my first visit there. Primarily because it's so difficult to find with something like Guilbaudian elusiveness - same side of Baggot Street Lower, curiously. After the hunt (2.15pm) I was to be disappointed .... most of the food stocks were depleted by the huns who'd been there from midday. You see, it's only open 11 ¼ hours per week - hardly worth the preparation and rental, you'd have thought. Soups, quiches, solid brown bread - good hearty food that satiates the baying white-collars. Advice to non-regulars - arrive early.
Babies/children catered for, child portions. Not wheelchair friendly. No smoking area (30). Booking advisable. Takeaway by arrangement. Ground floor. Stairs

Mitchell's Cellars
21 Kildare Street, Dublin 2
Tel 6680367
Seating 70
Open 12.15pm-2.30pm Mon-Sat; closed Sat June-Aug,
Average £10; house wine £7.95.
Payment all major credit cards; EC, TC
This lunchtime restaurant is the original cellar where Mitchell's the vintners bottled their wines. White-washed walls, casks and racked wines abound. The menu which changes daily has as its speciality quiche, but offers a starter of crab claws to be followed by lamb or beef. Be sure to leave room for dessert. A typical selection would be mocha cheesecake, lemon and almond meringue, raspberry crumble, fresh fruit salad and apricot frangipani. As it is a wine bar, you can expect lots of choice in this department with two different specials each month and they can also be bought by the glass (about £1.95), allowing the customer to taste different wines at a reasonable price. The Chateau St. Remy Frousac 1989 had a rich colour and warm texture, with a very dry aftertaste. Abbreviated opening hours

are not enough to deter the predominantly professional clientele who enjoy decent no-nonsense food.
Babies/children allowed. Not wheelchair friendly. No smoking area (18). Basement. Stairs.

Beaufield Mews Restaurant and Antiques
Woodlands Avenue, Stillorgan, Co Dublin
Tel 2880375
Seating 180
Open 6.30pm-10.30pm last orders Tues-Sat.
Average £16; house wine £9.50
Payment all major credit cards; EC, TC.
12 ½% service
Beaufield Mews, just south of Dublin city centre, is an 18th-century coachhouse which has retained its cobbled courtyard and possesses a resident, though somewhat feeble, spectre! Sheltered by tall trees and pretty gardens, this restaurant is more of a rustic retreat. The interior, with blackened beams, period furniture and an antique shop high up in the loft, fully supports this rural setting. Primarily an evening venue, lunch can be catered for and diners will enjoy traditional good food in a setting which, while spacious, retains elements of both intimacy and privacy. Included on the menu are well-loved entrées like salmon steaks, roast glazed duckling à l'orange, venison and pheasant in season. Their homemade ice-cream is made from scratch - a must for all dessert purists and finally, the accompanying wine list, while not over-extensive, is clearly carefully formulated, offering the customer a good choice
Babies/children catered for; high chairs. No smoking area (20). Booking advisable. Tables outdoors for aperitifs. Private parties catered for. Dress - collar and tie. Ground floor. Stairs.

Torulas Brasserie and Wine Bar
21 Railway Road, Dalkey, Co Dublin
Tel 2840756
Seating 35
Open 12.30pm-10.30pm Mon-Sat
Average £17; £16 set price meal; house wine £10.
Payment A, V; EC, TC.
Well off the beaten track in the romantic seaside village of Dalkey, Torulas offers excellent value and innovative cooking with a light touch. The menu changes regularly and often to accommodate seasonal finds and already this little-known gem has attracted the attention of those in the know by winning the attention of the plaudits. The wine bar, where a main dish can cost as little as £4, is a known congregation point for local celebrities. The upstairs brasserie, with its open fire, gives the feeling of being a guest in a friend's home. Vegetarian on request.
Babies/children catered for, child portions. Not wheelchair friendly. Booking advisable weekends Ground floor wine bar; stairs to brasserie.

Coopers Restaurant
8a The Crescent, Monkstown, Co Dublin
Tel 2842037
Seating 100
Open 5.30pm-11.45pm Mon-Sat; 4.30pm-10.45pm Sun
Average £16; house wine £8.75
Payment A, V; EC, TC.
10% service for eight or more
An interesting restaurant in an attractive location. It's Upstairs/Downstairs with dark beams and lots of curiosities. The conservatory provides another area of interest. The international menu changes frequently proposing items which include a steak sandwich at £5.50, fettucine for £3.60 and garlic bread at £1.60. Specialities include mussels tandoori, chicken Coopers style and duck, as well as vegetarian options.
Babies/children catered for, child portions and menu. No smoking area (20). Booking advisable Ground floor. Stairs.

Lady Ellen's Wine Bar and Coffee Shop
3 Anne's Lane, Dublin 2
Tel 8403107
Seating 27
Open 11am-12.30am Mon-Sat; 6pm-12.30am Sun
Average £10; house wine £10.
Payment TC, LV

This brand new brasserie style restaurant/wine bar, just off South Anne Street, is small and intimate with tablecloths and candles giving a warm feel. The varied menu offers dishes like paella and boeuf bourguinon, all delightfully presented. Perhaps its best feature is the fact that you can settle for either just a starter or a dessert.
Babies/children catered for daytime only, child portions; high chairs and baby changing room No smoking area (7). Booking advisable at night. Table outdoors. Wheelchair friendly. Private room for parties. Ground floor. Stairs.

Pembroke Wine Bar Restaurant
31 Lower Pembroke Street, Dublin 2
Tel 6762994/6762980
Seating 40
Open noon-midnight Mon-Sat; closed Sun
Average £12; £10 lunch and early bird; £15 table d'hote incl glass of wine; house wine £8.50.
Payment all major credit cards; EC, TC, LV.
10% service
Situated up a flight of stairs above the Pembroke Pub, you can nibble on a starter any time between noon and midnight, have a full meal or just the house wine or a pint. Another feature about this discreet little restaurant is the roof-top terrace - ideal for lunch on a sunny day.
Babies/children catered for. Not wheelchair friendly. No smoking area (8). Booking advisable. Tables outdoors. Takeaway by arrangement. Stairs.

The Footplate Brasserie
Heuston Station, Dublin 8
Tel 7032250/7032100
Seating 80
Open 10.30am-7pm seven days
Average £10.50; £9.50 set lunch; house wine £8.75. Fully licensed
Payment all major credit cards; EC, TC.
12 ½% service.
Restaurants or, in this case, brasseries in railway stations are noted for neither their ambience nor their fare. The Footplate is an exception - a swish brasserie with sanded pine floors, a raised seating platform and a 'punny' menu, nestles to one side of

Heuston Station, providing a popular lunchtime venue not only for travellers but also the local business community. The menu, although enormous in terms of physical size, is not huge in terms of choice. There are some fish dishes, steaks, pasta, not forgetting the ubiquitous burger. The tagliatelle al pesto is a healthy choice which will suit all tastes. Crushed pine nuts, basil, garlic and olive oil make up the sauce. It's worth arriving a little early for that next train down to Cork, even if only to glimpse what railway catering should be all about.
Babies/children catered for, child portions; high chairs. No smoking area (35). Booking advisable for lunch. Takeaway by arrangement. Neat casual dress. Ground floor.

Swedish Food Co,
43 Drury Street, Dublin 2
Tel 6799025
146A Capel Street, Dublin 1
Tel 8729670
146 Lower Baggot Street, Dublin 2
Tel 6785885
For delivery (att Elisabeth) Tel 6770878
Open 9.30am-5.30pm Mon-Fri; closed Sat/Sun; Capel St. open Sat.
Two Swedish sisters, who married Irish and settled here 27 years ago, finally last year decided to give us a representation of their country's cuisine in the form of three stand-and-demand outlets in the city. The Swedish Food Co, recognisable by its Swedish flag yellow and blue coloured exterior, offers a good sampling of native Swedish fare. The smorgasbord - a selection of dishes in small quantites, akin to Greek mezzes or Spanish tapas - served with brown bread, costs £10 per head and includes marinated Swedish herring (very unlike any Irish). Swedish meatballs, an anchovy and potato dish (again, very un-Irish) You can't really lose as you can try these in pristine clean conditions to decide if you like them before you buy ... Advice is to shelve your inhibitions.
Takeaway.

La Cave
28 South Anne Street, Dublin 2
Tel 6794409
Seating 35
Open 12.30pm-3pm Mon-Sat; 6pm-11pm seven days
Average £9.95, £5.95 lunch; £9.95 dinner; house wine £10
Payment all major credit cards; EC, TC, LV
A tiny cave in the middle of the busy Grafton Street area, full of interesting mainly French bits and pieces. They do good cheese plates, salamis and casseroles at reasonable prices and on Sunday night after 9.30, an assortment of local poets, actors and singers provide entertainment for the price of a glass of wine or a cup of coffee.
Not wheelchair friendly. Booking advisable weekends. Basement. Stairs.

Riverbank Restaurant
10 Burgh Quay, Dublin 2
Tel 6770162
Seating 90
Open 10am-11pm Mon-Thurs; closed midnight

Average £13.75 dinner; house wine £7.95.
Payment all major credit cards; EC, TC, LV.
10% service for eight or more.

This restaurant is one of those that's become a reference point to the compilers of **Edibilia**. Mention the Riverbank to Carolyn McGrath and you'll most likely be fishing her out of the Liffey. Not for any sinister reason, mind, like terrible food or appalling service, no, we just couldn't easily categorise it as anything ... we even contemplated requesting that the owner close up at 7pm just so we could erase our consciences and slot it cleverly into 'Daytime Only'. Edibilia HQ will reside there next year.

Babies/children catered for, child portions and menu; high chairs and changing facilities. No smoking area (15). Booking advisable. Private room for parties. Takeaway by arrangement.

Hotels

At one time, hotel dining rooms and burger bars were the only places to eat in Dubln . The rise of restaurant culture saw the decline of hotel food dominance and the departure of many of the old-stage chefs whose menus had remained almost the same since the thirties and forties.

Now new hotels and bastions of elegance like the Shelbourne attempt to woo with bar food and grill room alternatives. They're also recruiting younger staff who have returned with new ideas from stints abroad. Even the formal dining rooms where corporate lunchers tend to lurk have lost their starchiness. Hopefully, we've seen the last of the haughty headwaiter whose frosty greeting was "Have you booked?"

Small new hotels like The Hibernian and Longfield's are refreshing additions to the scene, run like the best of the countryhouse hotels with restaurants excellent enough to justify an independent existence.

The Grainne Uaile
Hotel Pierre
3 Victoria Terrace, Dun Laoghaire Co Dublin
Tel 2800291
Seating 50
Open 7.30am-10am breakfast; lunchtime; 6pm-10pm dinner.
Average £13.50-£16 three courses; £10 minimum 6pm-8.30pm; house wine £8.25.
Payment A, AmEx, V; EC, TC.
Located on Dun Laoghaire's seafront overlooking Dublin Bay, this hotel restaurant offers evening entertainment at the bar. Outdoor tables are provided for those who like to take the sea air when the weather is fine.
Babies/children catered for. Not wheelchair friendly. No smoking area (30). Booking advisable. Tables outdoors. Private rooms for parties. Ground floor.

The Doyle Tara Hotel
Merrion Road, Dublin 4
Tel 2694666
Seating 100
Open 7.15am-11pm seven days
Average £10; lunch £8 table d'hôte, £9.50 dinner; house wine £8.50.
Payment all major credit cards; EC. TC.
15% service
Popular with overseas visitors, the Doyle Tara Hotel, formerly Tara Towers, is a landmark on the Dublin Bay coastline, clearly visible from the B+I Ferry as it makes its way into port. Rooms facing the bay command fine views of Howth. The Conservatory Restaurant, as the name suggests, is chock-a-block full of plants. Although it is probably more akin to a coffee shop, it doubles as a grill, serving food best described as 'Traditional Hotel'. Specialities are Beefsteak Saute Strogonoff and Beef Wellington. Vegetarian available.
Babies/children catered for, child portions and menu; high chairs and baby changing room. No smoking area (30). Booking advisable. Private parties catered for. Ground floor.

Truffles Restaurant/Castle Grill
Fitzpatrick's Castle Hotel
Killiney Hill, Co Dublin
Tel 2840700
Seating 65
Open 12.30pm-2.15pm; 7pm- 10.30pm
Average £18 à la carte; £17.95 table d'hôte; house wine £9.50. Fully licensed.
Payment all major credit cards; EC, TC, LV.
15% service
Fitzpatrick's Castle Hotel, renowned for its sumptuous decor and excellent facilities stands in its own grounds nestled beneath Killiney Hill, overlooking Dublin Bay. The castle, built in 1741 as a residence for the Mapas family and later becoming an army garrison, is included in Harpers and Queen's '300 Best Hotels in the World'. The menu at Truffles Restaurant boasts dishes as varied as fresh rock oysters, venison and

specialities like flambéd steak and sole bonne femme. The Castle Grill, located in the dungeon, is far more informal with cane furniture and green walls contributing to a distinctive tropical atmosphere.
Babies/children catered for, child portions; high chairs at the Castle Grill. Not wheelchair friendly. No smoking area (16). Booking advisable. Private parties. Smart casual dress. Ground floor. Stairs.

Court Hotel - Killiney
Killiney Bay, Co Dublin
Tel 2851622
Seating 70 (restaurant); 65 (coffee shop)
Open 12.30pm-11.30pm coffee shop; 12.30pm-2.15pm, 7pm-10pm restaurant seven days.
Average £7.95 lunch (restaurant); dinner £17.95; house wine £9.50. Fully licensed.
Payment all major credit cards; EC, TC, LV.
12 ½% service
This hotel is set in its own gardens overlooking Killiney Bay which has been described as Ireland's Bay of Naples. The tasteful decor makes for an attractive dining room while appropriately, the walls of the library coffee shop are lined with shelves of bound books. The extensive restaurant menu is best described as French/Irish. Speciality fresh wild salmon. Vegetarian available. Favourites in the Library Coffee Shop include chilli con carne, sirloin steak, pizza, fresh scampi and chips.
Babies/children catered for, child portions and menu; high chairs. No smoking area (17) restaurant; (16) coffee shop. Booking advisable in restaurant. Private parties catered for. Dress - for restaurant - tie. Ground floor. Stairs and lift.

Powerscourt Room
The Royal Marine Hotel
Marine Road, Dun Laoghaire, Co Dublin
Tel 2801911
Seating 80
Open 7.30am-noon breakfast; noon-2.30pm (except Sat); 6pm-10pm.
Average £12 lunch; £17.95 dinner (both menus changed daily); £20 minimum à la carte.
Payment all major credit cards; EC, TC.
Overlooking Dun Laoghaire harbour and Dublin Bay, close to the car ferry terminal, the Royal Marine Hotel is located in spacious grounds beside a bowling green. Varied menu includes rib of beef carved from the trolley with roast potatoes and vegetables. Vegetarian available.
Babies/children catered for, child portions and menu; high chairs. No smoking area (20). Booking advisable. Private parties catered for. Neat dress. Ground floor. Stairs and lift.

O'Shea's (Moran's) Hotel
19 Talbot Street, Dublin 1
Tel 365670
Seating
Open 7.30am-10am breakfast, 12.30pm-3pm; 6.30pm-10pm dinner seven days.
Average £7.50; £ 2.75 breakfast; house wine £8.
Payment A, AmEx, V; EC, TC, LV.
A family-run 35-bedroom hotel within walking distance of Dublin's city centre, O'Shea's provides reasonably priced accommodation with en suite bedrooms. The pub offers free traditional and ballad music five nights and an extensive menu with dishes like steak and seafood and allows the traveller to sample Irish cuisine - Irish stew and bacon and cabbage
Babies/children catered for, child portions and menu; high chairs and baby changing room. Not wheelchair friendly. No smoking area (10). Private parties catered for. Ground floor.

Aisling Restaurant
The Shelbourne Hotel
St. Stephen's Green, Dublin 2
Tel 6766471
Seating 60
Open 7.30am-10.30am; 12.30pm-2.30pm; 6.30pm-10.30pm seven days.
Average £25-28 dinner; £14.50 lunch; house wine £11.50.
Payment all major credit cards; EC, TC.
15% service
Overlooking St Stephen's Green, the Shelbourne Hotel, reputed to be the best address in Dublin, is undeniably smart,

drawing native Dubliners and visitors alike to the Aisling restaurant which specialises in Irish cuisine.
Babies/children catered for, half price menu for under 15; high chairs. No smoking area (20). Booking advisable. Private parties catered for. Dress - smart.

Lord Mayor's Lounge
The Shelbourne Hotel
St. Stephen's Green, Dublin 2
Tel 6766471
Seating 50
Open from 8am seven days.
Average £3.50 morning coffee until noon; £8.50 light lunch; £6.75 afternoon tea 3pm-5.30pm; £2.95 Lord Mayor's sandwich selection; house wine £11.50.
Payment all major credit cards.
Afternoon tea in the Shelbourne is a familiar ritual for exhausted shoppers and visiting celebrities alike. The Lord Mayor's lounge, established in 1824, provides a suitably formal setting for traditional afternoon tea or a lighter cream tea, all to the accompaniment of live piano music.
Babies/children catered for, half price menu under 15. No smoking area (16).

Shelbourne Bar
The Shelbourne Hotel
St. Stephen's Green, Dublin 2
Seating 47
Open noon-9pm seven days.
Average £6.50 lunch; £4.50 bar menu daily; £9.50 pre-theatre special 5pm-9pm; house wine £11.50.
Payment all major credit cards
Extremely popular with both professionals and politicians, the clientele spill out into the lobby on weekend nights.
Speciality fish.
Babies/children catered for, half price menu under 15. No smoking area (15). Smart dress.

Aberdeen Restaurant
Gresham Hotel
O'Connell Street, Dublin 1
Tel 8746881
Seating 100
Open 7.15am-9.30pm seven days.
Average £17 dinner; £12 lunch; £12 executive menu; house wine £12.
Payment all major credit cards. 12½% service.
The Gresham, situated on O'Connell Street, the city's main boulevard, offers visitors a haven in the Aberdeen restaurant. Winner of a Galtee Breakfast Award, this international restaurant has an airy open plan interior, pale pink and white decor and is adorned with Irish art. Split-level seating allows diners to observe lobby activity or opt for privacy on the lower level. The varied menu includes salmon with champagne sauce.
Vegetarian available.
Babies/children catered for, child portions and menu. No smoking area. Booking advisable. Neat dress.

Toddy's Bar
Gresham Hotel
O'Connell Street, Dublin 1
Tel 8746881
Seating n/a
Open noon to late.
Average £11.50 dinner; house wine £12. Fully licensed.
Payment all major credit cards. 12½% service
An alternative to the Aberdeen Restaurant and reputed to have the finest selection of Scotch whisky in Ireland. An ideal meeting place right in the heart of Dublin 's shopping and entertainment districts. Delicious fish plates.
Babies/children catered for, child portions. Booking advisable for groups.

North Star Hotel
Amiens Street, Dublin 1
Tel 363136
Seating 50
Open 7.30am-10pm Mon-Sat; 8am-10am Sun; 12.30-3pm seven days; 5pm-11pm Mon-Sat; 5pm-10pm Sun
Average £10.00; £7.50 lunch; £10.50 dinner; house wine £9.50. Fully licensed.
Payment all major credit cards; EC, TC, LV. 10% service

Convenient to Dublin's major rail and bus stations, the North Star Hotel has welcomed many a weary traveller with its simple but gracious fare. Built in the 19th century, the railway theme is highlighted in the dining room decor.
Specialities include roast beef and steak. Vegetarian on request.
Babies/children catered for, child portions and menu; high chairs and baby changing room. No smoking area (8). Booking advisable. Private parties catered for.

Wynn's Hotel
35-39 Lower Abbey Street, Dublin 1
Tel 8745131
Seating 70
Open noon-3pm carvery lunch; 5.30-10pm dinner
Average £13; £9 lunch; £9 dinner; house wine £9.50. Fully licensed.
Payment all major credit cards; EC, TC, LV.
The hotel owes its origins and name to Miss Phoebe Wynn who, in 1845, opened a boarding house at 35 Lower Abbey Street in the house that had been the rectory for the parish church of St. Thomas. In the Murphy family since 1897, today there are 75 bedrooms all ensuite. An extensive à la carte menu features a range of international dishes as well as a selection of fish, grills and cold meats. Speciality is steaks
Babies/children catered for; child portions; high chairs. No smoking area (40). Booking advisable at weekends.

Central Hotel
1-5 Exchequer Street, Dublin 2
Tel 6797302
Seating 90
Open 12.30pm-2.30pm; 6.30pm-10.30pm seven days
Average £18.50 four course dinner; £10 lunch; £7.50 early bird 6.30pm-8pm; house wine £10.00. Fully licensed.
Payment all major credit cards; EC, TC.
12½% service
Located in the heart of Dublin's city centre, this top class hotel was established in 1887 and restored to its former splendour in 1991. Just a few minutes' walk from Dublin Castle, Trinity College, the Dail and a step away from Grafton Street, it houses a collection of contemporary Irish art. The brightly decorated dining room is divided by an arch offering a secluded area that can be used for small parties. The menu offers nouvelle cuisine in generous portions. Speciality is good seafood. Vegetarian available.
Babies/children catered for, child portions; high chairs and changing room. Booking advisable. Takeaway by arrangement. Stairs and lift.

Harcourt Hotel
60 Harcourt Street, Dublin 2
Tel 4783677
Open 12.30pm-2.30pm pub/carvery lunch and Sunday brunch; 5pm-9pm dinner seven days
Average £7.50 set lunch; house wine £9.50. Fully licensed.
Payment all major credit cards; EC, TC, LV.
Hotel restaurant. It is a popular lunchtime venue, serving the many offices in the area with evening meals served in the pub as well. Live musical entertainment nightly and there is also a night club open Tues-Sun.
Babies/children catered for, child portions; baby changing room. Booking advisable. Takeaway.

Russell Room / Sandbank
Westbury Hotel
Grafton Street, Dublin 2
Tel 6791122
Seating 95; 65
Open 12.30pm-2.30pm, 6.30pm-10.30pm Russell Room; noon- 2.30pm, 6pm-10.30pm Sandbank; both seven days
Average £14.50 set lunch; £11.50 Sandbank; £4.55 afternoon tea; £18.50 dinner; house wine £9.75. Fully licensed.
Payment all major credit cards; EC, TC.
15% service
The Russell Room specialises in French/ Irish cuisine, the Sandbank in seafood. Opened in 1984, The Westbury is the flagship of the Doyle Group and the only hotel restaurant in the Good Food Guide. Swiss-trained chef Patrick Brady produces a

predominantly French a la carte menu as well as a traditional table d'hote selection. Downstairs, the Sandbank is modelled on a typical Victorian Dublin hostelry, with a marble floor, huge central bar and typical clutter of nostalgia. A reasonably priced lunchtime dish of the day is served. Egon Ronay.
Babies/children catered for child portions; high chairs and baby changing room. No smoking area (30 Russell Room; 20 Sandbank). Booking advisable. Private parties catered for. Neat dress. Ground floor (Sandbank). Stairs and lift.

Castle Hotel
Great Denmark Street, Dublin 1
Tel 8746949
Seating 40
Open 7.30am-10am; 12.30pm-3pm; 6pm-9pm seven days
Average £3.50 breakfast; £2.50-£3.50 set price meals; house wine £7.95. Fully licensed.
Payment all major credit cards; EC, TC.
Although the Castle Hotel was founded in 1809, the Georgian house dates back to 1769. Under the present management since 1986, its central location makes it a popular choice for some of the major package tour groups who come for the legendary breakfast. Their vegetarian breakfast is a rare treat.
Babies/children catered for, child portions and menu; high chairs and baby changing room. Not wheelchair friendly. No smoking area. Dress neat. Ground floor. Stairs.

Hibernian Hotel
Eastmoreland Place, Ballsbridge, Dublin 4
Tel 6687666
Seating 45
Open 7.30am-10am, 12.30pm-2.30pm, 6.30pm-10pm Mon-Thurs; 6.30pm-11pm Fri/5Sat; 6.30pm-9pm Sun.
Average £12; £19.95 set dinner; £7.50 full Irish breakfast; £16.95 Sunday lunch. Fully licensed.
Payment all major credit cards; EC, TC..
A cross between a countryhouse and a gentleman's club, this new hotel with 30 rooms all ensuite is tucked away in Eastmoreland Place, off Upper Baggot Street, within walking distance of the city centre. Internationally trained chef Frederic Souty uses Irish ingredients whenever possible to produce a menu with a distinct French accent. Not a typical hotel dining room, the restaurant is bright and airy with a pleasant conservatory at one end. The menu changes with the seasons and homemade breads are served. Specialities are fish and confit of duck. Vegetarian on request.
Babies/children catered for, child portions; baby changing room. Bookings advisable. Takeaway by arrangement. Neat dress.

The Emily Room
Buswell's Hotel
24 Molesworth Street, Dublin 2
Tel 6764013
Seating 54
Open 7.30am-2.30pm, 6pm-9.30pm seven days; noon-2.30pm Mon-Fri
Average £13.50 dinner; £6.50 table d'hote menu; £10.50 6pm-8pm pre-theatre supper; house wine £9.50. Fully licensed.
Payment all credit cards; EC, TC. 12½% service.
Buswell's Hotel, founded in 1928 by Nora O'Callaghan Duff, mother of the current owner, still reflects many of the features of that era. The Emily Room restaurant, named after the Duchess of Leinster, whose town residence Leinster House is now Dail Eireann, reflects the spirit of the hotel with a Victorian charm and alcoved seating. The menu is also a product of this tradition so nouvelle cuisine is not to be expected.
Specialities are brown bread, homemade soups and desserts.
Babies/children catered for, child portions and menu; high chairs and baby changing room. No smoking area (18). Booking advisable. Private parties catered for. Neat dress. Ground floor. Stairs and lift.

Spinnaker Restaurant
Portview Hotel
Marine Road, Dun Laoghaire, Co Dublin
Tel 2844314
Seating 45

Open 5.30am-10pm
Average £14; £3.95 early bird noon-5pm; £6.95 three course Sunday lunch; house wine £8.50; glass £1.95. Fully licensed.
Payment all major credit cards; EC TC, LV.
One of the few places in Dun Laoghaire for al fresco dining during the summer months. Specialities are steak and seafood. Vegetarian available.
Babies/children catered for, child portions and menu; high chairs. No smoking area (14). Private parties catered for. Tables outdoors. Ground floor.

The Green Room
Dun Laoghaire Kingston Hotel
Haddington Terrace, Adelaide Street, Dun Laoghaire, Co Dublin
Tel 2801810
Seating 60-70
Open 6pm-9pm Mon-Fri; 6pm-10pm Sat; closed Sun.
Average £10.95 four course dinner; house wine £8.50. Fully licensed.
Payment all major credit cards; EC, TC, LV.
Service charge included.
Situated at the end of a terrace overlooking Dun Laoghaire Harbour, the hotel has won a Dun Laoghaire Tourism Award. There is live music in the lounge Mon-Sat. An attractive feature is the beer garden where barbecues are held in the summer and you can cook any fish you have caught in the Harbour while enjoying fantastic views over Dublin Bay. Offering international cuisine, chicken dishes are popular. Vegetarian available.
Babies/children catered for, child portions and menu; high chairs. Not wheelchair friendly. No smoking area. Booking advisable. Private parties catered for. Tables outdoors (beer garden). Ground floor.

Beecher's Restaurant
Deerpark Hotel
Howth, Co Dublin
Tel 322624
Seating 70
Open 6pm-9.30pm seven days; 8am-8pm coffee dock.

Average £12.00; £14 table d'hote dinner; house wine £9.00. Fully licensed.
Payment all major credit cards; EC, TC.
12 ½% service.
The Deerpark Hotel with three golf courses (open to all golfers at £10 per round), all set in the grounds of Howth Castle, commands stunning views of Dublin Bay. Part of the hotel, Beechers Restaurant is open to the public. The menu, which has a distinct international flavour and favours fish, changes daily. The spectacular views add to the whole dining experience.
Specialities are fish and steak. Vegetarian available.
Babies/children catered for, child portions and menu; high chairs and baby changing room. No smoking area (12). Booking advisable. Private room for parties. Neat dress. Ground floor.

Carvery Restaurant
St Lawrence Hotel
Howth, Co Dublin
Tel 322643
Seating 60
Open 12.30pm-2.30pm; 6.30pm-10.30pm seven days
Average £11.50 dinner; £6.95 set price lunch; house wine £7.95. Fully licensed.
Payment all major credit cards; EC, TC, LV.
A buffet which offers a large selection, ranging from hors d'oeuvres to include a roast joint, chicken or fish as well as a host of other dishes, ensures this restaurant's appeal to a wide variety of tastes. There is a discount for groups over 40 so it is ideal for corporate or family gatherings.
Speciality is roast beef. Vegetarian on request.
Babies/children catered for, child portions and half price menu; high chairs and baby changing room. No smoking area (20). Booking advisable. Private parties catered for. Neat dress. Ground floor. Stairs.

Russell Court Hotel
21-25 Harcourt Street, Dublin 2
Tel 4784066
Seating 50
Open 12.30pm-2.30; 7pm-10pm
Average £17.50; £9.95 set price lunch; £16 dinner; house wine from £9.50. Fully licensed.
Payment all major credit cards; EC, TC, LV.
12½% service at night only.
The hotel, which has been recently renovated, boasts a grand lobby and gilded Louis XIV furniture while the restaurant is still an art deco garden room where varied and interesting food is served. Conveniently situated just a few hundred yards from St Stephen's Green, there is also an outdoor beer garden which has been described as 'an oasis in a concrete jungle'.
Babies/children catered for, child portions; high chairs. Not wheelchair friendly. No smoking area (16). Booking advisable. Private parties catered for. Tables outdoors. Neat dress. Ground floor. Lift.

Embassy Garden Restaurant
Jurys Hotel
Ballsbridge, Dublin 4
Tel 6605000
Seating 104
Open 7am-10am, noon-2.45pm, 6.15pm-10.30pm seven days
Average £21; £11 twilight menu 6.15pm-7.15pm Mon-Thurs; £14-16 set carvery lunch/dinner Sun; house wine £15.50.
Payment all major credit cards; EC, TC, LV.
15% service
The excellent cuisine on offer is popular with followers of international rugby at nearby Lansdowne Road and visitors of the Horse Show at the RDS which is within walking distance.
Babies/children catered for, child portions and menu; high chairs. No smoking area (34). Booking advisable. Neat dress. Ground floor.

Clifton Court Hotel
11 Eden Quay, Dublin 1
Tel 8743535
Seating 65
Open noon-8pm seven days
Average £6.95; £7.50 four course Sunday lunch; house wine £7.95. Fully licensed.
Payment all major credit cards except DC; EC, TC.

Beside the hustle and bustle of O'Connell Bridge but unobtrusively situated, the low ceilinged dining-cum-bar area offers a varied menu complemented by a selection of bar food. Spotlit tables create an intimate atmosphere and weekend entertainment from 7pm consists of Irish ballads.
Babies/children catered for, child portions and menu. Booking advisable. Private parties catered for. Ground floor.

Parkers Restaurant
Lansdowne Hotel
29 Pembroke Road, Dublin 4
Tel 6606140
Seating 50
Open12.30pm-2pm Mon-Fri; carvery set lunch Tues-Fri; 6.30pm-10.30pm Tues-Sat; 6pm-10pm bar food; 12.30pm-2.30pm Sunday brunch. Fully licensed.
Average £13; house wine £8.50.
Payment A, V; EC, TC, LV. 10% service.
As Parkers, one of Dublin's newest restaurants, is attached to a hotel, a full selection of drinks is available. Starters include mussels with a lemon sauce and shrimps Spanish style - large prawns in a spicy tomato sauce. Main courses - Wicklow lamb with a rosemary and garlic sauce and seafood medley served with a large salad. For dessert, a meringue gateau in a strawberry sauce. Prices are certainly below average for a restaurant of this standard, whilst the food and service are truly above average. Vegetarian on request.
Babies/children catered for early evening, child portions; high chairs and baby changing room. Not wheelchair friendly. No smoking area. (20). Air conditioning. Booking advisable. Private room for parties. Takeaway by arrangement. Neat dress. Stairs.

Pubs

Irish pubs play a very unique role in the Irish social culture. So much so that we felt it necessary to devote a complete section to them in this guide - the only **Edibilia** edition in the series to do so.

There are literally thousands of pubs in the Dublin area - some small, intimate drinking emporia; others large commercial bar-cum-restaurants. But there's one common denominator: whichever pub you visit, you'll get a warm welcome and experience the *'caint, ceol agus craic'* (Gaelic for chat, music and fun) that have made the Irish pub scene famous all over the globe.

Naturally, we couldn't include every Dublin pub in this section - that would be a full guide in itself! Instead, we have randomly selected some of the better known ones to give just a flavour of the wide variety available.

There are pubs where you can quietly relax; meet friends and family; enjoy an evening's entertainment or have a meal. For the tradionalists, there is McDaid's, Toner's or Mulligan's in the city centre (to name but three), or for something more lively, try The Baggot Inn, the International Bar, The Wishing Well or any one of a number of the 'newer' hostelries around the capital.

'Pub grub' too is worth sampling - whether a quick lunch (toasted sandwiches are available almost everywhere) or an evening meal in an adjoining restaurant. Many pubs now offer a buffet selection at lunch time with hot and cold options for hungry tourists, shoppers and business workers.

Irish pub hours are 10.30am-11pm (Mon-Sat, winter hours); 10.30am-11.30pm (Mon-Sat, summer hours) and 10.30am-10.30pm (Sun, all year), with some closing for a few hours during afternoon and most being required by law to close from 2pm-4pm on Sunday afternoons.

Gate-Clock Pub
Area B Departures Gate, Dublin Airport, Co Dublin
Tel 8407466
Open 11am-10pm seafood
Payment TC
Traditional Irish pub. Entertainment - Irish traditional music on special occasions.
Babies/children allowed. Lift.

Cellarman's
The Dropping Well
Classons Bridge, Milltown, Dublin 6
Tel 973969
Seating 90
Open 12.30pm-2.30pm; 5pm-8pm evening bar menu
Average £12; house wine £8.95; corkage £4.
Payment all major credit cards; EC, TC. Fully licensed.
Pub restaurant. European style cuisine Specialities are steak, pasta.
Babies/children catered for, child portions and menu. No smoking area (20). Tables outdoors Basement. Stairs.

The Queens
12 Castle Street, Dalkey, Co Dublin
Tel 2854569
Open noon-6pm Mon-Sat; 12.30pm-2pm Sun
Payment A, V; EC, TC.
Pub, established 1745, whose original façade indicates the fine workmanship of the time The furniture, a mixture of oak and pine, complements the bric-a-brac and nautical memorabilia on display while the romantic 'old tavern' atmosphere is warmed by real fires. Cocktails served. As well as the usual bar food and hot lunches daily, there is also a Sunday brunch and regular jazz and traditional music sessions.
Babies/children allowed up to 6pm. Private room for parties. Tables outdoors. Ground floor. Stairs to function room.

The Mad Hatter
39 Main Street, Blackrock, Co Dublin
Tel 2887416
Open noon-2.30pm
Payment all major credit cards except DC; EC, TC, LV.
The pub is one of Blackrock's oldest surviving licences, going back as far as the 1770s, possibly much earlier as a coaching house. In keeping with its unusual name, the bar fascia was assembled from panelled doors of Irish Times filing cabinets, the counter top is made up of church pews and the bar floor was once a squash court. Regulars are known to turn up dressed as sheiks, toffs, cowboys and Indians! Cocktails served. As well as the regular lunchtime fare, there is also a Sunday brunch.
Babies/children allowed. Private room for parties. Tables outdoors. Ground floor.

The Yellow House
Willbrook Road, Rathfarnham, Dublin 14
Tel 932994/942554
Seating 60
Open 6pm-11pm Mon-Sat; lunch Sun
Average £12-15; £10 minimum price weekends; house wine £9.50
Payment all major credit cards; EC, TC.
Pub restaurant. Cocktails on request. Menu European/international. Speciality is fish - catch of the day.
Babies/children catered for, child portions and menu up to 7pm; high chairs. Booking essential weekends. Private room for parties. First floor. Stairs.

The Ass & Cart
31 Carysfort Avenue, Blackrock, Co Dublin
Tel 2880789
Seating 60
Open 11.30am-2.30pm carvery lunch; noon-5pm bar food.
Payment all major credit cards except DC; EC, TC, LV
Pub situated beside Frascati and Blackrock Shopping Centres; DART station and Blackrock village. Entertainment - traditional and contemporary music 9pm-11.30 pm Thurs, Sat and Sun. Corporate lunches a regular feature.

Speciality: seafood.
Babies/children allowed. Tables outdoors. Ground floor.

The 51
51 Waterloo Road, Dublin 4
Tel 6600150
Open 11.30am-2.30pm
Payment all major credit cards; EC, TC, LV
This premises acquired its first licence in 1843 under the guardianship of the Fleming family. It was the regular haunt Patrick Kavanagh and Brendan Behan and subsequently became popular with the young and fashionable who would visit the 51 prior to a night on the town in Leeson Street or other city nightspots. Its proximity to Lansdowne Road makes it a favourite pre-match watering hole and eating place. Frequented by local office and business people. Cocktails served.
Private room for parties. Tables outdoors. Ground floor.

Louis Delippes (formerly Bennigans)
South King Street, Dublin 2
Tel 4783266
Open noon-8pm
Payment all major credit cards; EC, TC, LV
Public and lounge bars. Cocktail bar. Entertainment: DJ Sun evening.
Babies/children allowed. Not wheelchair friendly. Stairs.

McCormacks - The Merrion Inn
188 Merrion Road, Dublin 4
Tel 2693816
Open noon-3pm seven days
Payment all major credit cards; EC, TC, LV
The Merrion Inn, opposite St Vincent's Hospital, has long been a landmark, well known as the M1 It was bought in early 1991 by Paddy and Eamon McCormack whose main pub is in Mounttown, Dun Laoghaire and reopened as McCormacks - The Merrion Inn, early December 1991. A real effort is

made in the food department - considerably better than regular pub grub.
Babies/children allowed. Private room for parties. Tables outdoors. Ground floor. Stairs.

Ashtons
Clonskeagh, Dublin 6
Tel 2600399
Seating 40
Open 6pm-9.30pm seven days
Average £15; house wine £9.95.
Payment all major credit cards; EC, TC, LV
Pub restaurant serving French cuisine menu. Vegetarian available. Cocktails on request. Very good food and popular for Sunday brunch and pre-match specials.
Babies/children catered for, ½ price child portions. Booking advisable weekends. Tables outdoors. Basement. Stairs.

Bentley Pub
163 Drimnagh Road, Dublin 12
Tel 557860/557533
Seating 200
Open 12.30pm-2.30, 5pm-8pm Mon-Fri
Average £4.65; house wine £8.
Payment A, V; EC, TC, LV.
One of Dublin's good food, drink and entertainment emporia that has been recently refurbished and located in the heart of Drimnagh, en route to the busy southbound roads. Voted the best pub food restaurant in Dublin, the Bentley is well-known for its fine cuisine and extensive lunch and dinner menus. Live bands play nightly except Fri and Sun. Speciality is carvery lunches.
Babies/children catered for, child portions and menu; baby changing room. Private room for parties. Takeaway. Ground floor.

Paddy Cullens
12/14 Merrion Road, Dublin 4
Tel 6684492
Open noon-2.30 toasted sandwiches; limited hot food - different special daily.
Payment all major credit cards except AmEx; EC, TC, LV.
Cocktails served.
Babies/children allowed. Private room for parties except Fri. Ground floor. Stairs.

Toner's
139 Lower Baggot Street, Dublin 2
Tel 6763090
Open 11.30am-3pm sandwiches and soup
One of the remaining 'genuine' Dublin pubs. Situated on the corner of Roger's Lane - named after the founder who developed the present pub as a bar and grocery shop, old stock drawers still remain behind the bar with some wares displayed in glass cases to the left and right of the door. This, we are told, is the only pub that W. B. Yeats ever entered. Apparently, he supped a sherry, then left. The decor, nicotine-stained walls and flagged floor, will take you back in time.
Private room for parties. Tables outdoors. Ground floor. Off licence

Bowes Pub
31 Fleet Street, Dublin 2
Tel 6714038
Open 12.30pm-2.30pm
Average £3.85 lunch main dish; house wine glass £1.70.
Payment LV.
Pub restaurant with roast adaily speciality.
Traditional Irish pub, with lots of dark wood, green-topped stools, is about 100 years old, borne out by its nicotine-stained ceiling. Central location and watering hole of Irish Times journalists. Worth a visit.
Private room for parties. Ground floor. Stairs.

The Baggot Inn
143 Lower Baggot Street, Dublin 2
Tel 6761430
Open pub hours
Average £1.20 sandwich; 90p soup.
Pub and live music venue. Dublin's rock pub situated close to Stephen's Green and the business heart of the city. Its association with rock music goes back a long while. This was where U2 started and not too long ago, David Bowie made an impromptu appearance. Celebrities mingle with regulars and there is a live band every night from 9pm.
Takeaway.

Neary's Pub
Tel 6778596
Open noon-3pm
Average £2.10 smoked salmon sandwich; house wine glass £1.85
Dublin's oldest theatrical pub. Cyril Cusack remembers standing at the door in the twenties, waiting for his father to come out of his drinking haunt. More recently, Michael Caine and Julie Walters lunched here whilst filming "Educating Rita". Renowned for its pint of real Guinness. Gaslights on the bar are a rare sight in Dublin today.
Private room upstairs for parties. Takeaway. Ground floor. Stairs.

The Duke
9 Duke Street, Dublin 2
Tel 6799553
Open midday-3pm lunch.
Average £4 lunch; £1.30 sandwich
The Duke has been on the street that bears its name for over 200 years. The street itself has been a favourite spot where Irish literary figures gathered over the years to take advantage of the publican's hospitality. Among those to have frequented the Duke were James Joyce, Brendan Behan and his rival Patrick Kavanagh. A place to visit when in the Grafton Street area.
Babies/children catered for, child portions. Takeaway sandwiches. Private room for parties. Grond floor. Stairs.

McGowans of Phisboro
18 Phibsboro Road, Phibsboro, Dublin 7
Tel 302650
Open noon-2.30pm; 6pm-closing seven days
Average £10.00 dinner; £3 bar snack baskets; £5.95 lunch.
Payment A, AmEx, V; EC, TC.
Pub restaurant strategically located close to St Michan's, the Law Library, Mountjoy Jail and a host of famous Dublin landmarks. In the McGowan family since 1949, the small public front bar is cosy with plenty of seats and an array of interesting theatrical posters. The big back bar favoured by the young and trendy who come for the wild, taped rock-music, tends to be very crowded. Unlike many pubs, the extensive menu is available until closing time, making McGowans a good eating, meeting and drinking place. Vegetarian available.
Babies/children catered for up to 7pm; high chairs. Smart casual. Ground floor. Stairs.

The Brazen Head
20 Lower Bridge Street, Dublin 8
Tel 6779549
Open noon-5pm; 12.30pm-7pm bar food
Average £4 lunch.
Payment A, AmEx, V; EC
The Brazen Head, one of, if not, the oldest pub in Ireland, is built on the site of a tavern dating back to the 12th century. Today, its fine collection of memorabilia makes for interesting browsing whilst sipping a pint. Vegetarian available.
Babies/children catered for up to 6pm, child portions. No smoking area (10). Takeaway. Private room for parties. Tables outdoors. Ground floor.

The Inn In The Park
174 Harold's Cross Road, Dublin 6w
Tel 922461
Open lunchtime; snacks up to 7pm
Average £6; £5 evening meals Thurs/Fri.
Payment A, AmEx, V; EC, LV.
Pub restaurant with live music every night except Tuesday when there is traditional dancing. The pub caters not only for functions like confirmations and 21sts, but, located opposite Mount Jerome cemetery, it is used for gatherings afterwards.
Babies/children catered for up to 7.30pm, child portions and menu. No smoking area (25). Private parties catered for. Takeaway. Ground floor.

Mother Redcaps
Back Lane, Christchurch, Dublin 8
Tel 533960
Seating 130 downstairs; 200 upstairs.
Open noon-7.30pm seven days; noon-3pm bar food Mon-Fri
Average £7
Olde worlde style pub-restaurant situated in the heart of the historic Liberties. Close to Christchurch, St Patrick's Cathedral and Guinness Brewery. Entertainment: live bands - traditional, jazz and blues Thurs - Sun. Cocktails on request. Specialities are Irish corned beef and cabbage, coddle, Irish stew. Vegetarian available .
Babies/ children catered for up to 6pm, child portions. Wheelchair friendly (except toilets). Private room for parties. Takeaway. Ground floor. Upstairs available but rarely used (except for gigs).

Davy Byrne's
2A Duke Street, Dublin 2
Tel: 6775217
Open noon-10pm bar food Mon-Wed, Sun; till 9pm Thurs-Sat
Payment A, V.
Lounge bar. Cocktails served. 1930s art deco pub in the Doran family for 50 years has been popular with successive generations of artists and writers. The licence is nearly 200 years old. Davy Byrne bought this pub in 1889 and put the name over the door. Murals of well-known Dublin faces painted by Cecil French Salkeld - Brendan Behan's father-in-law. Speciality: seafood
Only children over seven allowed. Wheelchair friendly (except toilets). Ground floor.

International Bar
23 Wicklow Street/8 Andrews Street, Dublin 2
Tel 6779250
Open 10.30am-8pm bar food
Payment TC
Public bar and lounge bar, cocktail bar downstairs. Entertainment nightly in separate room upstairs and on Sunday morning in the bar. Comedy two nights, music and plays during the day from 1pm-6pm. Soups and sandwiches served during winter; sandwiches during summer. In the Donoghue family since 1888.
Babies/children welcome till 7pm. Wheelchair friendly ground floor bar only. Booking advisable for upstairs bar. Private room for parties upstairs; advance booking. Tables outdoors. Off licence takeaway.

Kitty O'Shea's
23-25 Upper Grand Canal Street, Dublin 4
Tel 6609965/6608050
Open 10.30am-10pm bar food seven days
Payment A, AmEx, V; EC, TC, LV
Public-cum-lounge bar all in one. Entertainment nightly - Irish traditional music. Cocktails served. In 1981, this was the first pub in Ireland to introduce Sunday brunch between 12.30pm-2pm. Very significant rugby pub close to Lansdowne Road with high emphasis on food and revelry. Heavy sports influence. Extensive beer garden.
Babies/children welcome. Wheelchair friendly (except toilets). Private room for parties. Tables outdoors (200). Ground floor. Function room upstairs.

Bruxelles
7-8 Harry Street, Dublin 2
Tel 6775362
Open noon-2.30pm bar food; toasted sandwiches

till closing time
Payment EC, LV
Pub bar/saloon with Zodiac bar downstairs. Entertainment - international blues band, impromptu gigs. Built in 1886, cosmopolitan pub theme with hand-painted tiles.
Wheelchair friendly to top bar. Private room for parties downstairs bar (150 max). Ground floor, downstairs. Stairs.

Mulligans
8 Poolbeg Street, Dublin 2
Tel 6775582
No food
Payment all major credit cards
Established in 1782, this pub, probably Dublin's oldest and most famous, still retains much of its original early Victorian character. For years, Mulligans was closely associated with the Theatre Royal and many of its patrons were regulars, as are many journalists because of its proximity to two of the national daily newspaper offices. Mulligans is also part of the literary pub crawl which runs through the summer. Famous figures like Bing Crosby and Ted Kennedy have been known to sample a pint here.
Babies/children welcome. Wheelchair friendly (except toilets). Ground floor.

Dockers
5 Sir John Rogerson's Quay, Dublin 2
Tel 6771692
Open 12.30pm-2pm bar food; variety of sandwiches by request
Payment TC
Public bar/lounge bar done up like the interior of an old ship Cocktails on request. Entertainment - free rock music at weekends. Dockers is the local of Ireland's most famous rock group, (no names mentioned!), located aptly behind the Windmill Lane recording studios. Bought 17 years ago, its original character is still intact. Very popular with residents and tourists alike, weekends are 'manic' with fans hoping to glimpse a famous face or two.
Not wheelchair friendly. Ground floor.

The County Club
Braemor Road, Churchtown, Dublin 14
Tel 2960099
Open 11am-9.30pm bar food.
Payment all major credit cards; EC, TV, LC
Public and lounge bars with live music sometimes - jazz, traditional and rock. A bright and colourful pub, serving cocktails, with an upmarket menu, rather like a small restaurant menu than a large pub one. The County Club itself has always been a popular haunt for those in the Churchtown/ Dundrum area. Its nightclub, Faces, with a choice of three bars and now one of Dublin's leading hotspots, attracts young people from a large area. Good value Sunday lunch for the family.
Babies/children allowed. Private room for parties. Tables outdoors. Ground floor.

The Waterloo
36 Upper Baggot Street, Dublin 4
Tel 6600650
No food
Public and lounge bars refurbished in the

traditional style with frosted and stained glass fittings and tastefully designed mirrors. The mahogany bar and wall furniture complement the original ornate ceiling with its spherical lamp shades. Popular with those living and working in the area.
Babies/children welcome. Not wheelchair friendly. Ground floor.

Bellamy's
13/15 Ballsbridge Terrace, Dublin 4
Tel 6680397
Open noon-3pm lunch; 3pm-8pm dinner.
Payment all major credit cards; EC, TC, LV.
Public and lounge bars. Established since 1853 when Balls Bridge in the township of the Earl of Pembroke was no more than a tidy little village. Close to Lansdowne Road and the RDS as well as some of Dublin's leading hotels. Cocktails served. Entertainment: music 9pm-11pm Sun. Speciality: roast beef.
Babies/children allowed up to 6pm. Wheelchair friendly (except toilets). Private room for parties. Tables outdoors. Ground floor.

Old Stand
37 Exchequer Street, Dublin 2
Tel 6777220
Open noon-3pm; 5pm-9.30pm weekdays; noon-9.30pm Sat bar food.
Payment EC
Public and lounge bars. The Old Stand appears to have originally been a medieval inn and a favourite of John Philpot Curran, father of Sarah Curran, who was to become one of Ireland's most distinguished barristers. On a recent visit, Jeffrey Bernard hailed it as his favourite pub in the British Isles! Cocktails on request. Specialities: salmon and steaks. Ideal venue on matchdays and popular with office workers, business people.
Babies/children allowed up to 7pm. Smart dress. Ground floor. Stairs down.

McDaid's
3 Harry Street, Dublin 2
Tel 6794395
Open all day bar food mainly sandwiches
Payment EC
One of the great literary pubs of Dublin frequented by Patrick Kavanagh, Brendan Behan and Myles na Gopaleen. Entertainment: free music - blues and jazz.
Wheelchair friendly. Tables outdoors. Ground floor. Stairs.

The Step Inn
Stepaside, Co Dublin
Tel 2956202
Open 10.30am-11pm bar food.
Payment all major credit cards; EC, TC, LV
Tastefully decorated public and lounge bars which boast an interesting collection of artefacts and racing prints evocative of the association the house shares with nearby Leopardstown racecourse. Cocktails served. Entertainment: Sunday nights traditional and local musicians. Carvery and à la carte menu. Specialities are salmon in season, steaks and beef.
Babies/children allowed. No smoking area (35). Private room for parties. Tables outdoors. Ground floor.

The Norseman Pub
Temple Bar, Dublin 2
Tel 6715135
Open noon- 3pm; all day bar food.
Payment EC
One of the oldest traditional style pubs in Dublin. Its magnificent stained glass window, designed by French artist Isobel Payrat portrays a 'dream sequence' from James Joyce's Ulysses, and was specially commissioned by proprietor John Morris who has been responsible for The Norseman keeping intact its association with the Joycean era. Cocktails served. Entertainment - Sunday nights traditional Irish music, no cover charge.
Babies/children welcome up to 6pm. Tables outdoors.

Bleeding Horse
24/25 Camden Street, Dublin 2
Tel 4752705
Open noon - 3pm lunch; sandwiches
Reputed to be the second oldest pub in Dublin, allegedly licensed in 1649 (even before the Brazen Head). The Bleeding Horse was so called from the practice of bleeding a horse behind the ear to cure "head staggers". Rumoured that Joseph Le Fanu and Bram Stoker hatched the plot for 'Dracula' in this hostelry. Joyce, Oliver St John Gogarty and John Elwood all supped here. Newly restored with pitch pine and yellow pine everywhere, its secluded corners and nooks upstairs are popular with office crews for lunch. Its high ceiling is ideal for those with an aversion to smoke-filled ambience. Abundant brickwork and brassware. Food with Spanish flavour. Cocktails on request.
Babies/children allowed up to 7.30pm. Tables outdoors. Ground floor and upstairs lounge.

Sinnott's
Stephen's Green Centre, Dublin 2
Tel 4784698
Open noon-3pm.
Payment all major credit cards; EC, TC, LV
Public cocktail bar. The original pub stood at 3 South King Street and is now part of the Stephen's Green Shopping Centre. It boasts a comprehensive selection of literary portraits, collected by partner Michael Olahan. The central island back bar is actually a church altar and the marble foot rests came from a church as did the pine panelling on the walls which originated in Merrion Street Church.
Babies/children allowed up to 7pm. Not wheelchair friendly. Stairs.

Scruffy Murphy's
2 Powerscourt, Lower Mount Street, Dublin 2
Tel 6615006
Open 12.30pm-3pm; snacks in the evening
Average £6.50
Payment all major credit cards; EC, TC, LV
This old pub has been in existence since 1805 and Bridget Haydon, Licensed Grocer and Provisions Dealer was the first occupant of this house in what was a vibrant and thriving street of competing traders. Now classed as an olde worlde type pub with a smooth blend of wood and brick offset by traditional flagstone floor, it is not only a great rugby pub which serves a wholesome weekend brunch but it has a strong following of dedicated regulars. Cocktails served. Speciality: roast of the day.
Babies/children allowed up to 7pm. Private room for parties. Tables outdoors. Takeaway. Ground floor. Stairs.

Doheny and Nesbitt
5 Lower Baggot Street, Dublin 2
Tel 6760655
Open 11am-3pm
Average £6.50 lunch
Payment all major credit cards; EC, TC, LV.
A classic Dublin pub with Irish music on Sunday night. Originally a grocer's and vintner's run by William Burke in 1850, it was taken over by two friends, Doheny and Nesbitt, who returned to Ireland in the fifties and made this pub their life's work. It was during their stewardship that the pub became known as the "school of economics" because of the many prominent figures from business, politics and the media who would meet to put the world to rights. Two bars and myriad

reminders of the past. Vegetarian available.
Private room for parties. Ground floor. Stairs.

Auld Dubliner
24/25 Temple Bar, Dublin 2
Tel 6770527
Open noon - 2.30pm soup and coddle; sandwiches till 7pm.
Public bar. Irish coffee served. Entertainment - from 9pm during the summer Mon/Tues; 12.30pm-2pm Sunday traditional sessions.
Babies/children allowed up to 6pm at staff's discretion. Private room for parties weekdays. Ground floor.

The Cock Tavern
Main Street, Swords, Co Dublin
Tel 8405366
Open 12.30pm-2.30pm bar food
Payment LV.
Public bar and lounge bar.
Babies/children allowed up to 6pm. Not wheelchair friendly. Ground floor.

Playwright Pub
Newtownpark Avenue, Blackrock, Co. Dublin
Tel 2833969
Seating 150
Open noon-2.30pm Sun -Fri; 5pm-9pm Mon-Fri; noon-4pm Sat
Average £8; £5.50 lunch; house wine £8.60
Payment all major credit cards except DC; EC, TC, LV.
Pub restaurant with self-service bar food at reasonable prices. Outdoor barbecue area for those rare summer days. While lunches are geared to Sandyford/Blackrock business community, Sunday carvery is very much a family affair. Speciality: roast. Vegetarian available.
Babies/children catered for, child portions and menu; high chairs. Private room for parties. Takeaway by arrangement. Tables outdoors. Ground floor. Steps.

The Wishing Well Pub
20 Newtownpark Avenue, Blackrock, Co Dublin
Tel 2833970
Open noon-11.30pm Mon-Fri; noon-9pm Sat/Sun;
Average set price meal £2.50
Payment all major credit cards; EC,TC, LV
Friendly, busy pub nestling between the Dublin Mountains and Dublin Bay. Named after a large wishing well in the middle of a beer garden where - weather permitting - a barbecue fiesta is held. Indoors there are mahogany bars and counters, a cosy public bar and a tastefully decorated conservatory. Specials at £2.50 (e g barbecued spare ribs, chips and salad) are exceptionally good value. Speciality: carvery lunch. Vegetarian on request.
Babies/children catered for, child menu. No smoking area. Private room for parties. Tables outdoors. Ground floor. Stairs.

Mount Merrion House
Deerpark Road, Mount Merrion, Co Dublin
Tel 2623666
Seating 200
Open 12.30pm-9pm Mon-Fri
Average £4.50 main course; house wine £8.25
Payment all major credit cards; EC, TC, LV.
Mount Merrion House, a lunchtime haunt frequented by those working in the area, is close to Deerpark, which offers a marvellous panoramic view over Dublin on one hand and up to the mountains on the other. The hot beef sandwich (£2.50) is a meal in itself. Speciality is hot roast.
Babies/children catered for, child portions and menu. Tables outdoors. Private room for parties. Ground floor. Stairs.

The Rathmines Inn
89 Lower Rathmines Road, Rathmines, Dublin 6
Tel 970671
Open noon-9pm Mon-Fri; noon-7.30pm Sat-Sun
Average £4 main course; house wine ¼ bottle £2.20
Payment A,V; EC, TC, LV.
An interesting building in Lower Rathmines with a patio, which is rare for the area. Live music nightly from 9pm is an added attraction. Cocktails served.

Babies/children catered for, child portions. Private room for parties. Tables outdoors. Ground floor.

Goggins Pub
99 Monkstown Road, Monkstown, Co Dublin
Tel 2802735
Average £2.50-3
Licensed pub lunches. Specialities are homemade cottage pie, soups and light lunches.

Jack O'Rourkes Pub
15 Main Street, Blackrock, Co Dublin
Tel 2887102
Seating 80
Open 12.30pm-3pm; till 10.00pm food
Average £8; £2 minimum noon-3pm; house wine £9; ¼ bottle £2.25.
Payment all major credit cards except DC, EC, TC.
Pub restaurant. In the family since 1921, O'Rourkes is on the site of the principal inn in Blackrock where, in 1789, the first meeting of the Blackrock Association was held to take active action against the growing problem of highway robbers in the area. A favourite drinking haunt of Flann O'Brien (Myles Na Gopaleen), who lived in nearby Mount Merrion Avenue. There is a proliferation of Blackrock memorabilia decorating the walls. Good food in traditional 'old' Irish pub atmosphere; excellent fresh salmon open sandwiches. Speciality is fish in season. Vegetarian on request.
Babies/children allowed up to 7pm. Booking advisable. Private room for parties. Smart casual dress. Ground floor.

Stillorgan House
1 Lower Kilmacud Road, Stillorgan, Co Dublin
Tel 2882071
Seating 100
Open 12.30pm-2.30pm lunch
Average £4.50 main dish; house wine ¼ bottle £1.75
Payment A, V.
A typical pub with a lunch menu which generally features a roast. Especially suited for those who work in the Stillorgan area, or as a tranquil resting place after a busy shopping spree in the Stillorgan Shopping Centre.

Babies/children catered for, child portions. No smoking area (24). Private room for parties. Takeaway. Ground floor. Stairs to toilets.

The Old Punch Bowl
116 Rock Road, Booterstown, Co Dublin
Tel 2832356/2882042
Seating 80
Open noon-3pm; 7pm-10.45pm Mon-Sat; noon-10pm Sun
Average £5.50 carvery lunch £4.00; house wine £9.65.
Payment all major credit cards except DC; EC, TC, LV
When The Punch Bowl was first licensed in 1792 William Scully, then landlord, served such illustrious imbibers as the Fitzwilliams and the Viscounts Merrion. The pub takes its name from the vessel used to toast the victors of a local annual horse race. A haven on the busy coast road, its varied menu includes dishes like chicken korma, stir fry and traditional prawns in batter. Specialities are pot pourri of seafood, salmon roulade and fresh cod. Vegetarian available. Cocktails served.
Babies/children allowed up to 9pm, child portions and menu at lunch; high chairs. No smoking area (14). Not wheelchair friendly. Booking advisable weekend. Private room for parties. Tables outdoors. Stairs.

Druids Chair Pub
Killiney Hill, Killiney, Co Dublin
Tel 2857297
Seating 30
Open 12.30pm-3pm
Average £7.75; house wine £8.50; glass £1.75
Payment all major credit cards except AmEx, DC; EC, LV.
A pub restaurant that was originally a hotel and takes its name from the megalithic Druid's Chair on Killiney Hill behind it. Particularly attractive on a sunny day, near to Ayesha Castle, a splendid Victorian folly on the road down to the sea. The pub belonged to Mr Reagan - a fine figure of a man, who came back to Ireland from Liverpool after World War II and was well-known for generous whiskey measures. Speciality is roast. Vegetarian on request.
Babies/children catered for, child portions and menu. Private room for parties. Ground floor.

Stag's Head
Dame Court, Dublin 2
Tel 6793701
Open 12.30 pm- 3.30pm; 5.30pm-7.30pm; 12.30pm-2.30pm Sat
Average £5-6
Payment LV
This pub will be 200 years established in 1995. Traditional Irish food. Very popular with the Trinity set. Appears in many travel guides for its food - so don't be surprised to see puzzled bespoke Japanese. Speciality is bacon and cabbage. Vegetarian on request.
Babies/children catered for, child portions.

O'Briens
75-77 Ranelagh Village, Dublin 6
Tel 971351
Open 12.30-2.30pm Mon-Sat; 5pm-8pm Mon-Fri; not Sun
Average £5-6
Payment LV
Pub serving traditional Irish homemade food. Specialities: fish every Thurs/Fri, burgers and steaks.
Babies/children catered for, child portions.

Brady's Baker's Corner Pub
Baker's Corner, Kill o' The Grange, Co Dublin
Tel 2807782
Open 12.30pm - 2.30pm lunch; 2.30pm- 6.30pm bar menu Mon-Fri
Average £4.50 lunch main course; house wine ¼ bottle £ 2
Payment all major credit cards except DC; EC, TC, LV.
An olde worlde pub restaurant which serves as a local landmark. Serves enormous portions. Speciality is carvery roast.
Babies/children catered for, child portions and menu. Takeaway by arrangement. Private room for parties. Ground floor.

The Timepiece Pub
22 Temple Hill, Blackrock, Co Dublin
Tel 2888337
Seating 190
Open noon-2.30pm Mon-Fri; 12.30pm-2pm Sunday brunch
Average £3.50 main course lunch; £4.65 + coffee; £2.50 soup + sandwich + coffee; house wine £7.45, glass £1.85
Payment all major credit cards except DC, EC, TC, LV.
Pub restaurant with open plan kitchen. Popular pub for lunch with Blackrock office workers. 'Art Nouveau' decor. The 'Custom's House Clock', leftover from the 1922 bombing gives the pub its name. The scorched steel templates on the bar, a first in Dublin, set the trend which others have followed. Sunday Brunch at £4.50 includes a pint of beer. Cocktails served. Speciality is fresh home cooked food. Vegetarian on request.
Babies/children allowed up to 7pm, child portions, mini portions Sunday brunch. Booking advisable on Sunday. Private room for parties. Tables outdoors. Ground floor. Stairs.

The Green Blazer
Lansdowne Hotel
27/29 Pembroke Road, Ballsbridge, Dublin 4
Tel 6682522
Open noon-2.30pm; 5pm-10pm
Payment all major credit cards; EC, TC, LV
Hotel pub and cocktail bar situated in fashionable Ballsbridge. Entertainment: piano bar two nights; trad music with Sunday brunch.
Not wheelchair friendly. Private room for parties. Basement.

The Sarah Curran
Old Rathfarnham Village, Rathfarnham, Dublin 14
Tel 905481
Open 12.15pm-2pm
Payment all major credit cards; EC, TC, LV.
One of Dublin's most historic licensed landmarks, dedicated to the memory of local Rathfarnham girl, tragic heroine of Irish Romanticism through her relationship with Irish patriot, Robert Emmet. Situated in busy suburb, there is also 'Captain Chuckles', a Kiddies Fun House.
Entertainment: nightclub, Club Sarah, 11pm-2.30am Tues-Sun. Lunchtime carvery and family Sunday lunch.
Babies/children allowed. Private room for parties. Tables outdoors.

Palmers Pub
Golden Ball Tavern,
Kilternan, Co Dublin
Tel 2955643
Open 12.30pm-11pm
Payment A, V; EC, TC, LV
Entertainment: Irish set dancing, trad music, impromptu parties.
Babies/children allowed up to 7.30pm. Private room for parties. Tables outdoors. Ground floor.

O'Dwyers
8 Lower Mount Street, Dublin 2
Tel 6761718
Open noon-midnight
Payment all major credit cards; EC, TC, LV
One of Dublin's most celebrated pubs, the one primarily responsible for the return of the traditional pub back in 1980. Wall panelling in the back bar has been reconstructed from the jury box in Huddersfield Courthouse; chandeliers once hung in Maynooth Library and railings were part of a church in Co Wexford.
Generous portions of good wholesome food; brunch on weekend and match days. The Night Train, Dublin's first purpose-built live music venue for country blues is in the basement. Cocktail bar.
Babies/children allowed. Not wheelchair friendly. No smoking area (25). Private room for parties. Ground floor.

READER CONTRIBUTIONS

ıis is your opportunity to contribute to next year's guide and win a meal for two a top Dublin restaurant. Readers opinions are a valuable source for our comlation of this guide. Please tell us your experiences - good or bad - at Dublin's ting places.

All nomination forms will go into a draw for a number of meals-for-two at ıality Dublin restaurants. In addition, the establishment receiving most positive ›minations will be awarded ***Edibilia Restaurant of the Year.***

Report Form

Name..

Address...

....

....

....

Telephone ....

From my personal experience I do/do not recommend the following

establishment...

I had lunch/dinner there on (date) ....

Please list any relevant details (e.g. food, service, cost) or full review.

....

....

....

....

....

....

....

....

If you don't want to damage your copy of this guide, simply photocopy the forr
or you can get more forms by writing to the address below

Send all completed forms to this address:
Edibilia Publishing,
PO Box 3931,
Dublin 1.

Index

'51' Cafe and Deli 15
51 The 143
101, Talbot 75

A

Aberdeen 136
Adrian's Restaurant 122
Aisling The 135
Al Minar Tandoori Retaurant 38
Al's Restaurant 73
Alexandra Restaurant The 96
Ali Baba Restaurant 68
Alpha Restaurant 9
Ante-Room Seafood Restaurant 80
Applewood 2
Ashtons 144
Ass & Cart The 143
Auld Dubliner 152
Av20alon Grill 20
Ayumi-Ya Japanese Restaurant 64
Ayumi-ya Japanese Steakhouse 64

B

Bad Ass Bistro 28
Bad Ass Cafe 30
Baggot Inn The 144
Bamboo Home Delivery The 63
Baton Rouge 69
Batz 129
Beaufield Mews Restaurant & Antiques 130
Beechers Restaurant 140
Beggar's Banquet 13
Belinda's Coffee Shop 18
Bellamy's 150
Bentley Pub 144
Bernardo's Retaurant 49
Beshoff's 22
Bewley's 89
Bia 100
Bistro Pizza Pasta The 24
Bistro Vino 116
Bits & Pizzas 28
Blakes Restaurant 108
Blazing Salads 75
Bleeding Horse 151
Bon Appetit 92
Boss Crokers 112
Bowes Pub 144
Brady's Baker's Corner Pub 154
Brahms & Liszt 111
Brazen Head The 146
Break for the Border 68
Breakers Restaurant 120
Brokers Restaurant The 109
Bruxelles 147
Buck's Bistro 100
Buttercups Coffee Shop 16
Buttery Brasserie The 99
Buttery The 121
Buzz Cafe The 12
Byrne's Restaurant 21

C

Cactus Moon The 72
Cafe Carolina 128
Cafe Caruso 50
Cafe Crepe 17
Cafe Java 128
Cafe Kylemore 16
Cafe Ritz 19
Canaletto 104
Captain America's Restaurant & Bar 31
Casa Pasta 50
Cassell's Restaurant 123
Castle Hotel 138
Castle Vaults Bistro 85
Cavern Restaurant 113
Cedar Tree The 70
Cellarmans 142
Cellary Restaurant 76
Central Cafe 20
Central Hotel 137
Chandni Restaurant 39
Chanze Chinese Restaurant 57

Chapter One 85
Chavalee's Cafe 13
Chess Chinese Takeaway 64
Chewy's 7
Chicago Pizza Pie Factory 24
Chili Club The 66
Chimes 15
China China 55
China Cottage 63
China Palace Restaurant 58
China Sichuan Restaurant 61
Chompy's Deli Restaurant 8
City Arts Centre Cafe 88
Clarets Restaurant 101
Clarke's Restaurant 113
Clerys Department Store 4
Clifton Court Hotel 141
Cock Tavern The 152
Coffee Bean The 74+12
Coffee Deck The 15
Coffee Dock 129
Coffee Garden 12
Coffee Inn The 17
Coffee Shop The at IMMA 88
Coffers Restaurant 35
Colonnade 125
Commons Restaurant The 97
Continental Coffee Shop 11
Cooke's Cafe 98
Coopers Restaurant 130
Coopers, Kilternan 119
Coras Restaurant 45
Cornucopia 74
Corries Kitchen 8
Costa Coffee Boutique 15
Cottonwood Cafe 100
County Club, The 149
Court Hotel Killiney 135
Courtyard Restaurant 111
Cunningham's Coffee Shop 13
Curry Pot Coffee Shop 16
Curtlestown House
Country Restaurant 120

D

Daniels 116
Da Vicenzo 51
Davy Byrne's 147
Dee Gee's 122
deSelby's 115
Dillons Deli Restaurant 111
Dimples Coffee Shop 14
Dinty Moore's 5
Dobbins 92
Dockers 148
Doheny and Nesbitt 151
Dome Restaurant The 10
Dorset The 16
Doyle Tower Hotel The 134
Drop Inn The 4
Dropping Well The 142
Druids Chair Pub 154
Duggans Bistro 116
Duke The 146

E

Eastern Raga Indian Restaurant 39
Eastern Tandoori 40
Eddie Rocket's City Diner` 31
Embassy Restaurant 141
Emily Room The 139
Empress 60
Ernie's 91
Eureka Restaurant 67

F

Fans Cantonese Restaurant 56
Fat Freddies 26
Figaro's 5
Fitzpatrick Castle Hotel 134
Flanagan's Coffee Shop 4
Flanagan's Restaurant 112
Flash Harry's Diner 22
Floyd's Restaurant 116
Food Court The 21
Food for Thought 75
Food-Fair Restaurant 123
Footplate Brasserie The 131
Four Star Pizza 28

Fountain Restaurant The 4
Fox's Pub/Restaurant 81
Frederick's Restaurant 14
Frog City Diner 31
Fu Moon Chinese Takeaway 63
Furama 56
Fusciardi's 21
FXB 113

G

Gallagher's Boxty House 42
Gallagers Restaurant & Pizzeria 109
Galligans 6
Gammell's Delicatessen 17
Garden Bistro The 7
Garibaldi's 98
Gate-Clock Pub 142
George's Bistro 94
Gerry's 2
Giovanini Pizzeria Retaurant 49
Goat The 112
Goggins Pub 153
Golden Carp Chinese Restaurant 61
Good World Restaurant 55
Graham O'Sullivan 4
Grainneuaile The 134
Granny's Restaurant 96
Gray's 6
Green Blazer The 155
Greens Restaurant 115
Grey Door/Blushes 96
Guinea Pig Restaurant 79

H

Hanky Pancakes 17
Harcourt Hotel 138
Harrisons 42
Hibernian Hotel 138
Hot Plate 21
Hugh Lane Gallery Restaurant 87

I

Il Gabbiano 48
Il Primo 48
Il Ristorante 46
Imperial Chinese Restaurant 62
Independent Pizza 26
Inn in the Park The 147
International Bar 147
Irish Film Centre (IFC) 87
Ivy Court Restaurant 104

J

Jack O'Rourke's Pub 153
Jazz Chinese Restaurant 55
Jewel in the Crown 39
Jimmy Dean's 22
Joel's Restaurant 114
Johnson's of Dun Laoghaire 18
Judge Roy Beans 70
Juggy's Well 10
Jules Restaurant 65
Jumbo Takeaway 64

K

Kambo Takeaway 64
Kapriol Restaurant 49
Kebab House 22
Keeper's Restaurant 15
Kilkenny Kitchen 7
Killakee House 126
King Sitric Restaurant 80
Kingfisher Restaurant & Apartments 6
Kingsland (Dalkey) Chinese Restaurant 62
Kingston Hotel 139
Kingswood Country House & Restaurant 124
Kish Restaurant 80
Kites Restaurant 59
Kitty O'Shea's 147
Krishna Indian Restaurant 38

L

L & B Pizza Bar 28
L'Auberge 34
La Cave 132
La Finezza Restaurant 51
La Grenouille 36

La Mezza Luna 45
La Paloma 71
La Romana 47
La Stampa 93
La Taverna Restaurant 72
La Tavola Restaurant 52
Lady Ellen's Wine Bar 130
Lal Qila 38
Lane Gallery Restaurant 87
Langkawi 65
LaPizza 25
Lavins Restaurant 118
Le Caprice 48
Le Chateau Restaurant 123
Le Coq Hardi 37
Le Coquillage 103
L'Écrivain 36
Le Mistral 36
Legend Restaurant 59
Leinster Coffee House 13
Leo Burdock's 23
Les Freres Jacques 35
Levant The 70
Lido Cafe 19
Lighthouse Rooftop Restaurant The 81
Lisa's Trattoria & Restaurant 46
Little Lisbon 71
Little Moon The 105
Livingroom The 9
Lobster Pot The 79
Lock's Restaurant 92
Logan's 60
Lord Edward's Seafood Restaurant 80
Lord Mayor's Lounge The 136
Louis Delippes 143
Luigi's Fast Food 20
Luigi's Restaurant 50

M

MacNabs 103
Mad Hatter The 143
Malahide Castle Restaurant 122
Marks Bros 1
Mary Anne's Kitchen 11
Mary Rose Restaurant 10
Maxwell's 8
Mayfair Forte Grill 20
Mc Cormacks - The Merrion Inn 143
McDaid's 150
McDonalds 20
McGowans of Phibsboro 146
McGrattans 109
Meridian 125
Miami Cafe/Restaurant 19
Miller's Pizza Kitchen 25
Mimosa Salad bar 16
Ming Court 62
Mitchell's Cellars 129
Mother Redcaps 147
Mount Merrion House 152
Mountain View House 118
Mr Burger 22
Mr Hung's Sawadee Restaurant 65
Mr Hungs 63
Mr Tang Takeaway 63
Mullach Cottage Restaurant 81
Mulligans 148

N

Napoli Restaurant 46
Neary's Pub 146
Negi Restaurant 41
New York, New York 19
Niche The 3
Nicky's Coffee Shop 12
Nico's Restaurant 48
Norseman The 151
North Star Hotel 136
Number 10 34

O

O'Briens 154
O'Dwyers 155
O'Shea's (Moran's) Hotel 135
Odells Restaurant 117
Oisin's Irish Restaurant 43
Old Dublin Restaurant 98
Old Punch Bowl The 154
Old Schoolhouse The 124
Old Stand 150

Old Street Wine Bar 121
Oliver St John Gogarty 42
Omar Khayyam 69
Orchid Szechuan 63
Oscar Taylor's Restaurant 122
Oscars of Hollywood Bistro 106
Outlaws Rib & Steak House 33
Owl Restaurant The 17

P

Pacino's 52
Paddy Cullens 144
Paddy Kavanaghs 2
Paddy Whacks 119
Pagoda Restaurant 56
Palmers Pub, Golden Ball Tavern 155
Pantry The 14
Pappagallo's 27
Parker's 141
Partners Restaurant 119
Pasta Fresca 44
Pasta Pasta 50
Pastry Case Bakery/
Coffee Shop The 11
Patrick's Restaurant 109
Pavlova Pantry 12
Pembroke Wine Bar Restaurant 131
Penelope's Cake Shop 18
Penny Farthing The 14
Pepper Cannister Restaurant 118
Periwinkle 79
Phillers 1
Pigalle Restaurant 35
Piglets 11
Pings Restaurant 61
Pinheads Pizza 25
Pizza Cellar The 29
Pizza Connection 29
Pizza Express 28
Pizza Place 29
Pizza Stop 26
Pizzaworks 24
Pizzeria Italia 27
Playwright Pub 152
Plurabelle Brasserie 105
Poco Loco 67
Poppies 18
Powerscourt Room,
Royal Marine 135
Prince Restaurant 57
Priscilla's 16
Pronto Grill 112
Purdy's Pantry 7
Purty Kitchen 81

Q

Queens The 142
QV2 97

R

Raj Dhani Tandoori Restaurant 39
Rajdoot Tandoori 39
Rasa Sayang Oriental Restaurant 64
Rathmines Inn The 152
Refectory The 3
Relish Delicatessen 12
Restaurant Mahler 10
Restaurant na Mara 78
Restaurant Patrick Guilbaud 34
Restaurant Tosca 91
Ristorante Bucci 44
Ritz Cafe 19
River Moon Cafe 105
Riverbank Restaurant 132
Robinhood House Restaurant 124
Roccia Nera 46
Roches Bistro 93
Rock Garden The 30
Roly's Bistro 94
Roy's Restaurant/Guesthouse 18
Royal Garden Chinese Restaurant 57
Royal Tandoori 40
Ruby King 57
Russell Court Hotel 140
Ryan's of Parkgate Street 103

S

Salty Dog Restaurant 65
Sambos 3
San Marino 47

Sarah Curran The 155
Sayers Restaurant 110
Scruffy Murphy's 151
Señor Sassi's` 73
Shalimar Restaurant 40
Shelbourne Bar The 136
Shelley's Restaurant 6
Sheries Restaurant 31
Sherry's Delicatessen and Coffee Shop 13
Silks 58
Silver Lining Restaurant 123
Silver Service Restaurant 113
Singapore Gardens 58
Sinnott's 151
Sitar Indian Restaurant 39
Sounds Diner 21
South Bank Restaurant The 116
South Street Pizza 29
Spawell Lounge 110
Spinnaker Restaurant 138
St Lawrence Hotel 140
Stag's Head 154
Starvin' Marvin's Diner 33
Step Inn The 150
Stillorgan House 153
Subs 'n Salads 4
Subway 17
Swedish Food Co 132

T

Tá Sé Mohogani Gaspipes 104
Taj Mahal Indian Restaurant 40
Take Five 17
Tante Zoe 71
Tasty Options 3
Terrace Bistro 102
Timepiece Pub The 155
Toners 144
Torulas Brasserie & Wine Bar 130
Tower Restaurant 89
Trattoria da Mario 52
Treasures Takeaway 64
Tree of Idleness The 67
Trocadero 91
Trotters Restaurant 110
Trudi's Restaurant 117
Turret Restaurant 102

U

Unicorn Restaurant 47

V

Valparaiso Restaurant 71
Vertigo 129
Village Coffee Shop The 14

W

Waterloo The 148
Wed Wose 2
Weir's Restaurant 7
Welcome Chinese Restaurant 63
Wellfed Cafe 75
Westbury Hotel 137
Wicklow Arms The 118
Winding Stair Bookshop Cafe 89
Wings Chinese & Seafood Restaurant 60
Wishbone Restaurant 117
Wishing Well Pub The 152
Wok Inn, The 62
Wolfman Jack's 30
Woods 5
Wright's Brasserie 105
Wynn's Hotel 137

XYZ

Yellow House The 143
Zebra's 3
Zen Chinese Restaurant 63